Peace with Cancer

SHAMANISM AS A SPIRITUAL APPROACH TO HEALING

Myron Eshowsky

Shoshanna Publications

MADISON, WISCONSIN

Peace
with
Cancer

Copyright © 2009

Shoshanna Publications

P O Box 5203
Madison, WI 53705
www.peace-with-cancer.com
Contact: office@peace-with-cancer.com

Designed by Kristyn Kalnes in Madison, Wisconsin
Printed in the United States of America by United Graphics, Mattoon, Illinois

Library of Congress Cataloging-in-Publication Data

Eshowsky, Myron A.
Peace with Cancer: Shamanism as a Spiritual Approach to Healing/Myron Eshowsky

p.   cm.

Includes bibliographical references and index

ISBN 978-0-9793865-0-3
1.Cancer 2. Shamanism 3. Natural Health

10 9 8 7 6 5 4 3 2 1

Table of Contents

Acknowledgements

In the book, I make the statement that what we give love, we give life. The exquisite attention so many gave to the effort to create this book not only brought this book to life, they have all enriched me as well. As I learned so clearly in the process of writing, I now understand why writers say every book is a collaboration and reflects the attention and care people have given to its efforts.

MY GRATITUDES EXTEND TO my wife Karen for her belief in me, the work, and the importance of this book. As a physician, she was an invaluable resource as I, the non-scientist, struggled to understand what I was reading in my research. More importantly, the many hours spent talking about what I was writing and her insights were precious and lovely beyond what I can say here. More than anyone she helped flesh out what I was trying to convey.

Pam Spence for her careful editing of the book, as well as, her patient ear in those moments of questioning and self doubt. Roan Kaufman for his teaching and showing me the process of how a book gets done. Kristyn Kalnes for her beautiful layout and design work.

Cecile Carson for her friendship, poignant feedback and questioning of what I was trying to convey. Her ability to view the book as a physician and a shamanic practitioner offered the best of both worlds. To Niraj Nijhawan, M.D., for his insights regarding remission in cancer. Our discussions of the state of health care in this country were enlightening and helpful. To Roby Rogers, M.D., for her help and suggestions in what to read about oncology and cancer research. To Kimberly McCarthy, Ph.D. for her feedback and thoughts from the perspective of Positive Psychology. To Jonathan Mills, Ph.D. for his encouragement of the book both from the perspective of shamanic practice, but also his own struggles with cancer.

To the many clients and students along the way that have taught me much of what is reflected in this writing. Dawn Korten, Mary Reddy, Pam Spence, Roan Kaufman, George and Nancy Egger for your feedback and suggestions when I needed them along the way and most of all, the support you extended throughout.

To my great aunt Soshie for helping me hold on to my dreams. To my father who in his quiet way gave me some important lessons which has influenced all of my work.

About the Author

Myron Eshowsky, M.S., is an author and consultant. He has written and published in a wide range of professional journals on topics related to the integration of shamanic methods to modern problems. His work has primarily focused on the question of how to bring healing to severely traumatized populations. He has provided consultation and healing services to community mental health centers, prisons, social service agencies, tribal governments, NGO's, hospitals, universities, the United Nations and corporations. Additionally, he has taught throughout the United States and Europe. He was the first shamanic practitioner in the United States to be covered by a health insurance plan specifically to provide shamanic healing.

MYRON ESHOWSKY, M.S.

Introduction

The rhetoric of war is so prevalent in modern narrative that it influences how we think about day-to-day life. War-like words are used freely in politics, sports, medicine and relationships. Yet ironically, we associate peace with death. So what would happen if we shifted our consciousness from 'being at war with cancer' to approaching it with peace, understanding, and healing? That question is the backdrop to this book. My intention in writing the book is to offer spiritually empowering methods to help people address cancer and other chronic illnesses. It is in no way meant to be a substitute for medical treatment and care. Instead, it offers a complementary approach that has proven useful in promoting the best possible outcomes. Throughout the book, I will be providing suggestions and exercises to promote spiritual learning and healing.

THE STORY BEHIND THIS BOOK

Years ago a man approached me asking, "What do you know about healing work with cancer?" When I asked him what had motivated him to ask the question, he shared that he had lost his wife to cancer. I saw that he carried the burden of deep pain because he could not do more for her. Moments like these often elicit an internal response that says, " pay attention". Because his question struck a deep chord in me, my mind began to organize itself around the question, "What have I learned about healing and cancer?"

Ironically, his question came to me almost thirty years to the day after my father died of cancer. My father was a veteran of World War II. Like many from his generation, he did not like to talk about the war. Yet the war was a profound part of his dying process. In the weeks before his death, his outward behavior revealed his memories of the war. At the time, I was struck with the idea of the war on cancer. While President Nixon declared war on cancer, my father was fighting his cancer by re-fighting World War II.

I reflected on a number of cases where I had either counseled people or provided healing services for them. Through the years I've worked with Viet Nam veterans with non-Hodgkin's lymphoma, people with AIDS and Kaposi's Sarcoma, survivors of the Chernobyl nuclear reactor disaster with thyroid cancer and leukemia, residents exposed to radiation from nuclear bomb test sites and other toxins. I saw all kinds of people with all types of cancer for all sorts of reasons. I watched as some people went into remission while others maintained their health and vitality well beyond expectations. Ultimately, those who found peace within themselves, were at peace with dying.

What began as a question sparked a quest to take the things that were helpful in my healing work with cancer and put them in a form that could be readily accessed by others. In preparation for writing this book, I also read a wide range of literature on cancer and cancer treatment from mainstream and alternative medical perspectives. I did this, in part, to find common ground and similarities in approaches. Like any review, this led me down a path of discovery and integration. In any type of spiritual inquiry, there are questions to be explored. My inquiry included looking at those cases where patients either went into remission or lived vital lives well beyond what was anticipated. I reflected on all the cases that came to mind. I considered how each case presented itself in its spiritual manifestations and how that guided the approach we took in our work together I explored how traumatic events, what shamans refer to as soul-loss events, contributed to illness. Knowing that certain ecological conditions could contribute to increased occurrences of certain cancers I looked at how earth-based forms of spirituality viewed illness in relation to the environment. Despite the relatively minor occurrences in which genetic factors trigger cancer, I wanted to understand the shamanic perspective on this as well. Through it all, the most important question was always, "What factors lead to the best outcomes?"

The Institute of Noetic Sciences (IONS) has done a significant amount of research on the characteristics associated with remission and survival, as reported by cancer survivors. Some of the these, as listed on their website, are:

A change from dependency to autonomy combined with activities, attitudes, and behaviors that promote increased autonomy,

awareness of themselves, others, and their environment, love, joy, playfulness, satisfaction, laughter, and humor.

Facing the crisis, the despair, the sadness, and the pain and discovering they have the power to find a new way of life that is fulfilling and meaningful.

Taking control of their lives, (personal, professional, emotional, spiritual, and medical) and living each day fully combined with a willingness to evaluate their beliefs and attitudes and change old beliefs and attitudes that are no longer appropriate or adequate.

Becoming comfortable with and expressing and accepting both their positive and negative emotions/feelings, their needs, wants, and desires (physical, emotional, and spiritual); the ability to say "No" when it is necessary for their well being.

Having at least one strong loving relationship—a strong connection to another person, an activity, an organization(s): changing the quality of their interpersonal relationships with spouses, friends, family, neighbors, doctors, nurses, etc. in a positive way, and motivation to help others.

Working in partnership with their physicians and participating in decisions related to their health and wellbeing.

Finding meaning in the experience of cancer, finding reasons to live, accepting the diagnosis, but not the prognosis, seeing the disease as a challenge, belief in a positive outcome, and having a renewed desire, will and commitment to life.

Choosing activities and practices that promote increased awareness and reduce stress (imagery, stress reduction, yoga, etc.); showing renewed spiritual awareness (Soul) that often results in a spiritual practice (prayer, meditation, religious affiliation, a connection to nature, etc.).

Upon reading this research, it became clear to me that a shamanic-based approach complements the IONS findings, and, in many ways, offers a unique perspective to the healing journey.

SHAMANISM, SPIRITUAL LEARNING AND HEALING

Shamanism is the oldest form of spiritual practice and healing known to humankind. A shaman, according to Mircea Eliade in his classic text on shamanism, "specialize in a trance during which his soul is believed to leave his body and ascend to the sky or descend to the underworld."[1] This state of trance, which American anthropologist, Michael Harner, calls a shamanic state of consciousness, allows the shaman to embark on a shamanic journey. Shamanic journeying is a method in which a person encounters spirits and the spirit realm. In shamanism, the spirits are fundamental in understanding the spiritual aspects of illness and the processes used to alleviate suffering. Michael Winkelman notes:

"Shamanism, one of humanity's most ancient traditions, has recently re-emerged in contemporary societies' religious, spiritual, and healing practices and consciousness traditions. Although specification of the basis and nature of shamanism has often been vague and ambiguous, there is a broad recognition of a primordial natural form of healing and personal development with continued relevance for today's world."[2]

Harner suggests that an "important reason that shamanism has wide appeal today is that it is spiritual ecology."[3] This is particularly relevant in a world where environmental pollution is a significant contributor to cancer rates. While some of the healing perspectives of shamanism are presented in the book, the primary emphasis is on working with our own spiritual helpers toward health and healing. By using the trance-based spiritual imagery methods of shamanism, individuals partner with their spirit helpers to work with their illness, confronting cancer and other chronic illnesses that may reside in their bodies. As you'll discover, healing requires a strong fighting spirit along with a mindful approach to peacemaking. In this context, a fighting spirit means shoring up the internal strength to face and address the challenges in your life in a proactive compassionate manner. The overall premise is that the philosophy and methodology of shamanic and tribal healing practices embody many of the key variables cited in the Institute of Noetic Sciences research.

Chapter one gives a historic overview of war and cancer, illustrating how the consciousness of war pervades much medical thought. It also delves deeper into what has been known about carcinogenic environmental exposures for more than seventy years. And it shares a spiritual empowerment model for working with cancer. Chapter two explores the terrain of trauma and how our bodies respond to traumatic events in our lives. It theorizes that trauma factors heavily into creating the conditions that allows cancer cells to develop. Chapter three looks at shamanism as the original trauma medicine and explores some of the healing methods used in healing work with cancer.

As we move into chapter four, the emphasis is on using spiritual imagery, i.e. shamanic journeying, and different healing techniques that can support the healing messages revealed in those journeys. Space is provided for you to write notes on your journeying experiences. Chapter five examines the unique role that "places" and environment play in shamanic traditions of healing. It explores how places can become spiritually sick and how that sickness can affect the people who come in contact with them. The spirits of nature offer a different healing approach for you to explore. Chapter six addresses issues of death and dying, while also suggesting methods for working with 'death anxiety.' It also looks at the idea of "death as healer".

The case examples and names are written in a way that protects the privacy of the individuals involved. In some instances, the cases are composites of several similar cases. The purpose is to provide examples that you can contrast your own experiences against. As you read the book and the case studies ,however, it is important that your attention remain primarily on your spiritual experience rather than those presented in the book. If you find you're having trouble processing what happens in the journeys and understanding the spiritual information you unearth, I recommend that you work with a professional counselor familiar with the use of imagery and spirituality. If you go to **www.peace-with-cancer.com** you can download free drumming to use in your shamanic journeying. The following two books are great resources should you want to learn more about shamanic journeying:

The Way of the Shaman by Michael Harner

Shamanic Journeying: A Beginner's Guide by Sandra Ingerman

This book and its approaches are not an alternative to working with your physicians and other health care professionals. It is meant to complement that work. Ideally, you should work with professionals who are willing to consult with each other and who are open to a variety of approaches. Beware of people who offer miracle cures and guarantee outcomes or who push you to not work your physicians.

Peace
with
Cancer

CHAPTER 1

Cancer as War and Peace

*"The words we speak of
are powerful. They have their own power. When we treat them—
use them dishonestly or without care—they can do serious harm
to ourselves and others."*—Ratu Noa, FIJI ELDER

In a dream I had years ago, Winnie the Pooh and I were sitting alongside the bank of a pond. Winnie turned to me and said, "You use powerful words. Do you work out?" I gave him a bewildered look and simply shook my head, "no." "Words are like houses," Winnie said, "Some people use so many words that they do not know where they live."

No matter how they are shaped, molded, formed or framed, words have power. Few words evoke more fear in people than "cancer." As a word, it is used to describe over two hundred types of cancer, no matter how slow, aggressive, or life threatening it may be. Its power lies in our response to the word itself. Cancer is a house that few of us care to live in.

Many will constrict in fear. Some will want to battle for their lives and refuse to give in while others may collapse and accept death as their fate.

Many cancer survivors have shared that spirituality and the emotional support received from loved ones, friends and professionals were essential to their positive outcomes. Yet words long associated with spirituality have been trademarked and watered down through advertising and sound bites. "Joy" has become a dishwashing detergent. "Miracle" is now an automobile wax product. Most of us don't associate joy with cancer and most believe a miracle is needed when the cancer word invoked.

Cancer is an illness of a body at war with itself and ,historically , has brought a medical response of war. Western physicians respond by speaking of the "war" on cancer and stating that "we are going to treat this aggressively." Armed with weapons of surgical precision, chemotherapy, new medications whose aim it is to cut off the blood supply lines to cancer, and radiation, Western medicine fights the fires of a cancer burning and eating away at the body with its own versions of fire. The war terminology associated with cancer also has power. Whether this power is positive or negative is one of the questions we will examine in this book.

The World Health Organization reports that worldwide cancer will be the leading cause of death by 2010. Lung and prostate cancer are the top killers for men in the United States. Cancer fatalities are highest for U.S. women with breast or lung cancer. One in two men in the U.S. will be diagnosed with cancer at some time during his lifetime. One in three women in the U.S. will be diagnosed with cancer in her lifetime. Once thought of as a disease of old age, the age of cancer onset has been dropping since World War II.

Shamans have long known what we do to the Earth, we do to ourselves. Many say the malignant behaviors of humans towards the Earth brings malignancy to us as humans. Most cancer is not inherited but made by how we as humans live on earth. In general, causation factors are broken down into four general categories: genetics and family history; obesity and dietary habits; environmental influences; and lifestyle factors.[1] It is estimated that 5-10 per cent of all cancers are linked to genetic factors.

Dr. Servan-Schreiber cites a study completed in Denmark where a detailed genetic register traces each individual's origins. Published in the New England Journal of Medicine, the researchers found that in the case of adoptees, biological parents who had died of cancer prior to age fifty had no influence on adoptee risk of developing cancer. At the same time, comparable adoptive parents who died prior to age 50 of cancer had a significant influence on adoptees developing cancer. The researchers concluded it was the habits of the parents that had profound influence in the rate of vulnerability to cancer.[2] Dr. Servan-Schreiber concludes there is much we can do to protect ourselves.

"Tragic sins become moral failures only if we should have known better from the onset," says Jared Diamond, evolutionary biologist and author. In the case of cancer that certainly has been true. Since the International Congress of Scientific and Social Campaign Against Cancer in 1936, it has been known that agents such as arsenic, benzene, asbestos, synthetic dyes and hormones, and ionizing and solar radiation were known to be cancerous for humans. For over seventy years, it has been known that cancer is rarely inherited and reflects an illness of how we live on earth.

During the first six years of the twenty first century, the United States tripled its imports of asbestos from China, Brazil, Columbia, and Mexico, despite the fact asbestos has been banned due to research that correlates asbestos exposure to the development of mesothelioma. Research reveals numerous examples of communities where chemical pollution and radioactivity of the air, water, and land have led to higher rates of cancer, leukemia, and other environmental related illnesses. While many remember the toxic pollution found at Love Canal or the wide swath of radiation exposure from Chernobyl, other contaminated places, such as the Louisiana delta towns of Mossville and Reveilletown, were bought up by major chemical corporations who never admitted their pollution had rendered the communities uninhabitable. Despite the alternatives of surgery, chemotherapy and radiation as treatments, it remains true to this day that the best survival and quality of life outcomes are via early detection and prevention.

Devra Davis, author of *The Secret History Of The War on Cancer*, notes that Americans in their twenties today carry in their bodies levels of chemicals that can inhibit their ability to produce healthy children as well as increase the chance these children will develop cancer. The Centers for Disease Control and Prevention (CDC) has confirmed that American children are being born with dozens of chemicals in their bodies that did not exist a couple of decades ago. There are numerous examples of communities where the chemical pollution and radioactivity of the air, water, and land have consistently led to higher rates of cancer and other environmental related illnesses.[3] New cases of cancer not linked to smoking or aging are on the rise. Examples of this are cancer rates in children and non Hodgkins lymphoma in people older than 55. The CDC now lists cancer as the number two cause of death for children and middle age adults. Accidents are number one.

The goal of this book is to share a shamanism based model that works to restore balance and harmony; brings peace and healing as a response to illness (versus war); and offers empowerment to cancer patients. The approaches draw upon more than thirty years of healing work with cancer patients including, but not limited to, Vietnam veterans with non-Hodgkins lymphoma (Agent Orange exposure), Chernobyl survivors and others exposed to radiation such as Gulf War veterans via depleted uranium, farmers and farm workers exposed to pesticides, and persons living near environmentally (chemically) contaminated land and/or rivers.

HEALING FROM THE WAR

In the early 1970's, I spent a year with my father as he went through his struggles with cancer and subsequent dying process. What started out as colon cancer metastasized to the bones and brain. Contemporary Western medicine notes that as cancer cells conquer an area of the body they send out scout cells whose function it is to find territories of the body in which to establish new colonies. Slowly but consistently I watched the war of cancer spread throughout the territory of my father's body.

My father remained a strong warrior with dreams of a positive future until the doctors said they could do no more. As a family member, I was forced into a conflict with the doctors to get them to tell my father that the cancer conquered his body and their battle was over. When the primary care doctor agreed to tell my father, I watched the power of those words speed his ending. Something deep inside my father cracked and his grip on reality was gone. His last remaining weeks were spent re-living World War II, a defining traumatic moment in his life.

My father like many World War II veterans never talked about the war. I'd hear him screaming in the night when he would have flashback dreams of the war when I was growing up. I couldn't help but be struck by his reliving and again battling the war he had fought as a young man while his body fought the war within. I sat there during the remaining weeks watching the war he relived as the only way he knew how to process the losing battle in his soul.

In those weeks while my father fought World War II in his mind, he lost his ability to be oriented to the reality around him. Somehow he knew who I was while most others were gone from his mind. As he relived the war, the terror that I imagine he previously had repressed to emotionally maintain went unabated. Most of the time I could not discern whether he was screaming from pain caused by his cancer or from reliving his war trauma.

I would try to match my father's rhythms as a way of trying to connect with him. I had spent 25 years of my life trying to know this man and now could only connect in all the indirect ways. Words had always failed between my father and myself. I would mirror his breathing, his volume, his cadence, and his story. I lived the war with him as a way of trying to understand the unspoken history of my father's life. We re-fought the Battle of the Bulge together. When we came upon peasants, we would speak in German to try to trick them. We'd capture and interrogate these once real German paratroopers who were disguised as local peasants. Together we dodged bullets and bombs. Together we would help the wounded and get them to safety. We visited a concentration camp together and cried for the survivors we spoke with whom we spoke Yiddish. The emotional pain at times was excruciating. I was so captured by this experience, it took over my dreams and began to dream the battles we lived in together.

In those weeks of living the past as the present, I drew closer to the man that had been an enigma much of my life. I came to know how much he had been shaped by war and how that had been a barrier to my knowing my father. On the last day of his life, he returned briefly from the war and said "I love you." It was the only time I heard those words directly from him. And I think in his own way, he found some peace between us before his death.

At the time, it was the early days of President Nixon's declared "War on Cancer." I thought at that time, my father had finally become a casualty of war. In my own mind, the war had finally killed him albeit indirectly. His way of coping with the post war traumatic stress was smoking, eating poorly and living a relatively unhealthy lifestyle. It was a classic combination for triggering cancer.

CANCER AS WAR

Cancer as a process looks so much like war. It is not surprising the medical treatment response mimics modern warfare. Cancer lies dormant in each of us. An invasive exposure to toxic agents such as chemicals, radiation, or viral mutagens can be the triggering factors that lead to alterations in DNA sequences. Cancer develops when two or more sequential DNA "hits induce gene mutations that promote growth or confer a survival advantage to the affected cell and its descendants, collectively called a malignant clone."[4]

War is not an event that occurs spontaneously. The underlying factors of the conflict are invisibly at work until they ignite past the boiling point. Cancer as an illness develops over years until finally it has grown to a level that its existence is acknowledged. Once in cancer's grip, the whole body is at war. Cancer cells, says Dr. David Servan-Schreiber, are like "armed bandits roving outside the law."[5]

In general, cancer cells are extremely fragile in nature and easily controlled by the body's natural defense systems. Inflammation is a natural occurrence of one's immune system countering injury or invading foreign substances. Cancer cells also produce highly inflammatory substances (cytokines, prostaglandins, and leutokines) in order to induce inflammation which they need to sustain their growth. The inflammation acts like chemical fertilizer which promotes further cancer cell production. Cancer needs blood to thrive and cancerous tumors need their own blood flow for further growth so they create blood vessels of their own (supply lines).

When the body detects a foreign body or outsider (antigens) the Natural Killer (NK) cells of the immune system gather around the invaders and seek membrane to membrane contact. Once they make contact, NK cells aim their internal equipment at their target. They are capable of killing different types of cancer cells. When cancer overwhelms an area, the NK cells stop trying. Additionally, cytokines released by cancer cells, if elevated for prolonged periods of time, can impair the immune system's detection and predispose a person to developing cancer. High levels of cytokines are frequently observed in critically ill persons.

Like fire, cancer needs to be fed, as it is fragile by nature. Fire will do whatever is necessary in order to stay alive. As cancer conquers an area, it begins to send out scout cells seeking new territories to conquer. Cancer metastasizes and spreads. To metastasize, cancer cells leave their anchorage site and invade a blood vessel or lymphatic channel. Once these scout cells find a new site, they establish a new tumor colony and attempt to trigger new blood vessel formation so they can grow and spread. It is estimated that approximately 30 percent of cancer patients have detectable metastases when first diagnosed. Another 20–30 percent of cancer patients will have metastases reveal itself later in the course of the disease.

Ironically, chemotherapy as treatment for cancer was discovered via an observed side effect of mustard gas on veterans of World War I. In evaluating the few men who survived mustard gas attacks after the war, researchers discovered that they had extremely low white blood cell counts. Medical researchers considered the similarity of this finding to the disease of leukemia, which is characterized by excessive white blood cell counts. They then searched to find a way to dilute mustard gas so it could be used as a medicine to lower the white blood cell counts associated with leukemia. While researchers knew that mustard gas had side effects such as nausea and hair loss, thus began the development of chemotherapy.

Since the 1930's, with the rise of the Women's Field Army established by The American Society for the Control of Cancer, the United States and other countries have used the rhetoric of war in the treatment and prevention of cancer. Funding and research has primarily flowed toward the goal of killing and wiping out cancer.

THE COSTS OF WAR

Cancer as war means facing the certainty of illness and all of the possible consequences. When we think of the negatives aspects of war, we conjure up images and words of destruction, suffering, devastation, loss of control and safety, death, and grief. There are costs to any war, both in economic and human terms.

The National Institutes of Health estimated the overall costs for cancer in the year 2000 was 180.2 billion dollars. Of that total, 60 billion dollars was for direct medical costs. Lost work productivity due to illness was 15 billion dollars, not including lost years of potential productivity due to premature death. Cancer related costs account for ten percent of the total amount spent on disease treatment in the United States. In financial terms, cancer can be viewed as an economic burden for the patients, an economic investment by the healthcare industry, or as a source of revenue for those who are involved in any aspect of the treatment of cancer.

The war language related to cancer has had its own set of consequences. Despite the knowledge of environmental agents contributing to certain types of cancer since the 1930's, the war approach to cancer treatment moved funding priorities away from research and prevention.

As Devra Davis notes:

"The prospect of massive unrestrained global conflict fundamentally changed public priorities and altered the way science was supported and used by those who underwrote its efforts. The immediate need to defend against threats of Axis conquest trumped consideration of the longer term results of living crisis-driven lives. To be concerned with preventing cancer requires planning for and thinking about what will happen in a few decades. A world facing highly uncertain, potentially cataclysmic, prospects was not inclined to ponder the future."[6]

The war on cancer has had its share of commentators who have argued the war on cancer has focused too much on the wrong targets. Samuel Epstein argued in *The Politics of Cancer* that the war was focused on the wrong target. He argued that the primary cause of cancer was chemical and physical environmental agents and that the focus should have been on prevention. Dr. Guy Faguet, Professor Emeritus of Medicine at the Medical College of Georgia agreed with Epstein but also argued against the cell kill paradigm that has dominated the research and treatment debate. There is another argument that oncology is a business. In the U.S. today, we use three times more on drugs in cancer treatment than in other countries, and spend five times more on chemotherapy. The U.S. cancer survival statistics are not appreciably different from other industrial societies.

When we look at the costs of the war on cancer in human terms, the issues and questions begin to change. How does one respond to the cancer diagnosis? How do family members, friends, co-workers respond to learning that one has been diagnosed with cancer? How does one address the trauma of facing and undergoing treatment? How does one live with the possibility of recurrence if they are in remission?

Its important to recognize not every one responds in the same manner. The uniqueness of each person's personality, personal history, and soul is revealed when first diagnosed. Once again, we look at the power of words. The range of response to being diagnosed with cancer can be shock and numbing, anger, sadness and loss, or denial and fight at all cost. Life and death have their own ways of defining who we are. Both test our souls and offer opportunity to know ourselves deep inside. Yet cancer as a word can define a person. One becomes a cancer patient or a cancer survivor. Thus, cancer can become a form of identity and a role one plays in life.

The identification with illness in its own way feeds itself. In the early 1980's I had opportunity to meet Norma Jean Orlando, a psychologist at Elgin State Hospital in Illinois. She was primary researcher for a study whereupon staff were screened to live in a mock psychiatric ward. They were to live as patients and follow the same kind of structure and programming typically followed at the hospital. Twenty-nine staff members were confined for three days in the mock ward. In a short time, the mock patients began to operate similarly to real psychiatric patients. Six tried to escape, two withdrew into themselves, two wept uncontrollably, and one came very close to having a nervous breakdown. Most experience increases in anxiety, tension, frustration and despair. Most reported feelings of being treated as less than a person, not being listened to, and not being treated with caring as a person. Similar studies have looked at what happens when one is identified as an inmate in a mock prison. The question raised by these studies is how much does the identity with cancer elicit a response of hopelessness and despair.

Once identified as being a person with cancer, one now faces the prospects of war. Like soldiers on the front, the anticipation of waiting and living in the unknown puts the mind and body under tremendous stress. The war on cancer elicits its own imagery of wounds, scars, and possibly death. Wounds may come in the forms of hair loss , nausea from the chemotherapy, or the lack of energy. Scars may be surgical incisions or the loss of parts of one's body. Scars can also be the eating away at the body by the cancer cells themselves.

Like every war, there are the invisible scars. The kind of scars that disturb the sleep through nightmares or morbid thoughts. Like war veterans, dreams may come back reliving traumatic moments in the battle to stay alive. Yet unlike the war veteran, there are no hospitals and services when you return home from your service to the country. No parades to welcome home the embattled from their meetings on the battle fronts of cancer.*

*An exception the author wishes to note are the yearly Susan B. Komen Breast Cancer Walks which is like a parade and honors all cancer survivors.

Rarely do you find articles speaking to the post war consequences of cancer and the needs to heal the terrain of one's psyche and soul.

Not every soldier comes back from a war with severe PTSD, nor does every person with cancer. Those who fought closest to the field of battle tend to have the hardest time. One could only speculate that the intensity of the cancer and treatment process is somewhat similar. The cancer, even when treated successfully, remains a living presence in one's life. Cancer remains a permanent possibility. For some it is like a demon that evokes fear. As a demon, it lurks in the shadows waiting for opportunity to feed once again on the mind and body through fear and worry as well as returning to feed again on the body.

HEALING FROM THE WAR

Most of us when we think of healing from cancer, we think of a cure i.e. medical treatment that gets rid of all evidence of the disease. Dr. David

Servan-Schreiber strongly suggests it is equally as important to heal the terrain that fostered the possibility of cancer. Addressing the terrain of the body and soul is a process of multi leveled healing.

Healing is an inner process seeking wholeness. As Michael Lerner shares:

"Healing can take place at the physical level, as when a wound or broken bone heals It can take place at the emotional level, as when we recover from terrible childhood traumas or from death or divorce. It can take place on the mental level, as when we learn to reframe or restructure destructive ideas about ourselves and the world that we carried in the past. And it can take place at what some would call a spiritual level, as when we move toward God, toward a deeper connection with nature, or toward inner peace and a sense of connectedness."[7]

Shamans in traditional spiritual forms of healing focus on healing the soul so the body actualizes its own natural ability to heal. They believe healing the soul restores vitality and allows the body to have the energy it needs to heal. They work with compassionate and healing spirits without attachment to outcome, yet fully believing healing may take place when cure is not possible or proven impossible. Spontaneous remission studies of cancer cases remind us repeatedly as baseball player Yogi Berra once said, "It ain't over 'til its over."

For shamans too facing the fear of illness and death with the help of healing spirits is at the core of their practice. Facing death and rebirth with the helping spirits is the means of gathering spiritual knowledge and power. And for some who heal from their illness, it may be their initiatory calling into working as a vessel of the spirits.

Julie Silver, M.D., in her book *What Helped Me Get Through: Cancer Survivors Share Wisdom and Hope* states that often patients share with her they don't have time for healing as their lives are consumed by work and family. She stresses that taking time to heal is important. She cites research showing the importance of religion and spirituality in causing chemical changes that support the immune system's ability to do what it does best. She devotes a chapter in the book to spirituality.

Survivors reported a number of ways they felt spirituality was helpful such as: helping keep a clear mind; provide an avenue to do soul searching; finding the inner strength they needed to face their illness; gain an increased sense of connectedness with God or others. Spirituality becomes a means through which to explore the numerous questions which emotionally arise within someone facing cancer. A recent journal article found that spirituality influenced all aspects of the cancer experience for a group of men with prostate cancer. These spiritual practices included personal ceremonies, indigenous healing rituals, prayer, meditation and the use of spiritual based imagery.[8]

In the coming chapters, we will explore a spiritual empowerment model for persons with cancer and other severe chronic illnesses. Key variables to the model are:

1. Moving away from identity with one's disease is seen as a critical variable for empowerment and healing. Identity doesn't come from diagnosis or roles we have in life. It comes from one's relationship with self, family, community, and Spirit. The alliances we create provide the core of support necessary for best possible outcome.

2. Seeks to heal the terrain of the soul as a contributing factor to who gets sick. Cancer is not a single causation illness, but rather a constellation of factors in relationship to each other triggering cancer cell growth. Spiritual healing of the soul seeks to restore balance and harmony so the body's natural ability to heal is restored.

3. Provides a focus on what a person can do to actively embrace their illness and methods for working spiritually to support one's own healing.

4. Explores illness as a reflection of collective issues all of us share as opposed to only focusing on the individual. Looks at the spiritual wisdom of indigenous beliefs such as "what we do to Mother Earth, we do to ourselves."

5. Approaches cancer and other severe illnesses from a peace-based model of response. A peace-based model doesn't rule out the need for utilizing aggressive treatments. It does, however, raise questions as to the potential damage of waging war first before taking a bigger picture view of who the person who is sick and how did they get to this place in their life.

CHAPTER 2

Shamanism as Trauma Medicine

"The art of peace is medicine for
a sick world. There is evil and disorder in the world because people
have forgotten that all things emanate from one source. Return to
the source and leave behind all self-centered thoughts, petty desires,
and anger. Those who are possessed by nothing possess everything."
—Morihei Ueshiba, FOUNDER OF AIKIDO

THE WAY WE WALK

The Halakah Approach is a shamanism-based approach to cancer that in-corporates peacemaking traditions, current psychological understandings, modern medicine, and other spiritual traditions. *Halakha* is a Hebrew word, which, literally translated means, "the way we walk." The way we walk in our personal lives and the way we walk collectively on the earth both affects our health.

In traditional cultures, illness is thought to arise from a constellation of disturbed relationships between: body and soul, individual and family and ancestors, the invisible realms of Spirit, and the individual with the Earth. These disturbances lead to separation from the interconnections which support the vitality of life. All illness, from a spiritual view, is about separation from ourselves, the world around us, and the Creator. Our greatest wound is the belief that we are separate and lone.

LIVING IN A WORLD OF SEPARATION: A Teaching Story

As a child, I grew up in a working class neighborhood with lots of children around. Some of the older boys were very much into defining what it meant to be a man. The worst thing was to be called a sissy. The boys picked on the girls and put down anything associated with girl activities. The older boys fixated on tormenting outdoor cats, which they saw as girlish. As the one in power, Dennis determined what was said, what knowledge was shared, and how one was to act. So when he yelled, "Kick that sissy pussy!" his followers kicked the cats high into the air and laughed mercilessly. The cats screeched, their fur sticking straight out as they tried, unsuccessfully, to escape to safety. It was painful to watch and no one dared cry, lest they be called a sissy. With every hit and kick, I saw light forms jump out of the cat's bodies. Shamans call this phenomenon soul loss.

Eventually, the battered cats stopped being loving creatures. Over time they lost weight, stopped grooming themselves, and screeched loudly when anyone come near. Attempts to approach them, even with the most loving intentions, would bring arched backs, fur standing up, and an amazingly loud hissing sound that hurt the ears. The cats' sense of disconnection extended to each other as well as to humans. They became loners.

Each day I fed the cats by putting pieces of hot dogs or other Lunchmeats on a plate that I snuck out of my home. In the early days of trying to feed them, they didn't come to the plate of food. At the time, I thought it odd that they would be so hungry but not come immediately to eat. I had to leave the plate in the middle of the backyard and retreat to the house. As I watched from the kitchen window, I saw them slink along the ground like snakes, slithering slowly toward the plate. Every few inches forward, the cats looked in all directions to make sure the coast was clear. It was a dance of safety, which moved to an inner heartbeat, a pulse of fear.

This food ritual always took a long time. Once the cats reached the plate there were extraordinary detailed movements to ensure the coast was really clear. Before taking even little bites, the cats repeatedly sniffed the food, their need for safety overriding their pangs of hunger. Every bite was synchronized with head movements to the left and then to the right: a ritual that helped them establish the safety of the meal. After months, the cats would finally come to me when I put out the plates of food. But if I tried to extend my hand to pet or comfort the cats, their backs would go up and the hissing would begin. Violence was all they associated with an open human hand. Love and kindness did not heal their many deep wounds. Around this same time, a new family consisting of an ex-GI, his Japanese wife, and the couple's two young children moved into the neighborhood. In the hierarchy of hatred it was worse to be a "yellow Nip" than a "sissy, so there was a lot of derogatory talk about these young children.

One day, the neighborhood bullies got the idea to get the Nips. Images of World War II movies and John Wayne were invoked in which there could be no greater evil than a "Jap." Group fervor rose to a fever pitch in the desire to wipe out the evil element. It took on religious undertones, with proclamations like "God would want us to do this," and "These are Christian-hating people who killed American heroes." Soon it was as if an energetic wave of hatred pulled all the boys into action against the Japanese American children.

Everyone was picking up a rock to chase and throw at those little kids. I saw the wide-eyed look of terror on their faces, and just like the cats, I watched the light jump out of their bodies as they tried to run away. I was so taken with the terror in their faces that I froze in my tracks. After a brief moment I walked away.

I walked to some nearby fields in an area that had once been a wetland. At the end of the fields stood a grove of old oak trees where I often hid. I loved the feeling of getting my hands in the soil and crumbling the earth between my fingers. The scent was delicious. I felt comforted as I sat in the middle of the trees and chanted. Rocking back and forth, I drummed on the earth. In my imagination a giant mist rose, and I dreamed that an ancient man appeared before me.

Words could never do justice to this old man's presence. He was large and thin, his face covered with a long white beard, and he was draped in billowing rich, deep purple robe. His eyes sparkled like bright lights, and his gaze gave me a sense that he knew me deeply and accepted me. I felt completely safe. In that moment I shared the burdens in my heart with him.

"Why do they hate so much? "I asked. Very plaintively he said, "They do what they have been taught. What have you seen and what have you learned?"

I felt a nauseous wave flow from my belly up my back. I explained, " The cats, the Japanese children: they had this wild look in their eyes and their lights jumped around all over the place. And I felt sick inside while I watched." He nodded and sat silently for what seemed like a long time. "But what about the ones who hate?" he said. "What did you see in them?"

I pondered this question, replaying the recent incidents in my mind, and what haunted me were their eyes. "Their eyes look like the cats, like the Japanese kids. " He looked at me and simply said, "Then you have learned something about fear." In my young mind, it was beyond my comprehension that the bullies were afraid.

Later I told this whole story to my great aunt Soshie, whom I adored. She was very old, yet full of sparkle. Soshie took my hand into hers and we sat on her bed. She always asked me to tell her a story, and when I told her this one, she simply said, "That is the world of separation."

CONNECTION AS HEALING

We need to understand that as spiritual beings we influence the world just as we are influenced by the world around us. To move toward healing of cancer and other illnesses, it is critical to address this world of separation. Sometimes we'd like to make cancer or our doctors the enemy so we can distance and separate ourselves from that world. Doing so, however, gives us a false sense of safety. If we instead look for more common ground we can find true healing. If we bring ourselves into relationship with cancer or other illnesses, we can learn how to bring true healing change.

Shamanic spiritual healing traditions are based in understanding how we, as human beings, survive the difficulties of living and the effects those challenges have on our souls. These healing traditions seek to reconnect us to our sense of aliveness, wonder, and curiosity. They connect us to the web of life. These approaches call upon the compassionate intervention of the spirits to bring healing to sickness in a non-violent manner. Non-violent does not mean passive, as work with the spirits is active. This activism can take on many forms and does not preclude the sense of fighting an illness. We can confront our illness by being an active participant in medical treatment, finding the strength we need through gathering good information and seek-ing the support of others. Many of the practices presented in this book will provide opportunities to develop personal and spiritual strength.

TRAUMA AND CANCER

The 20th century was the most violent and polluting century in the history of humankind. Yet not everyone who is exposed to trauma, or environmen-tal carcinogens, or radiation develops a serious chronic illness. Cancer cells are within each of us, so what is it that determines which bodies will be able to eliminate these cells and which ones will go on to develop malignancy?

Achterberg, Simonton, and Simonton note:

"...It has become increasingly clear that not only is the development of the malignant cell influenced by external agents (viruses, carcinogenic materials, etc.) but also that the appearance of clinical malignancy is in-fluenced by the immunological competence or resistance of the host."[1]

This speaks to the complex causation of cancer as a disease. There is not one cause but rather a relationship of forces at work. When a person is exposed to prolonged stress or intense trauma, the body reacts through hormonal shifts and subsequent immune system suppression. The immune system can be-come overwhelmed and lack the energy to react to cancer cell expansion.

Psychologist Lawrence LeShan noted that it was a widely accepted view during the eighteenth and nineteenth centuries that severe emotional trauma contributed to the onset and development of cancer. More recent research (P. Balthwell and A. Manovani, 2001; Harold Dvorak, 1986) revisited these 19th century ideas and found there may be some basis for this thinking. Dr. David Servan-Schreiber suggests this research makes a case for the traumatic events in our lives being part of the terrain that contributes to cancer's development. He advocates an approach to cancer treatment, which includes healing the contributing trauma issues via counseling.

While the incidence of cancer continues to increase with age, more and more cancers are occurring in people in their thirties and forties.[2] Two potential causes of this are the dramatic increase in everyday exposure to carcinogenic agents since the 1940's and increased incidents of trauma and shock.

Even the nature of war trauma has changed dramatically in the last half century. Now more than half the casualties of war are women and children. Rape increasingly occurs in war. Harvard University researcher Kaethe Weingarten describes the violence and trauma in our world as "common shock." She feels that violence in its many forms has become so commonplace that most people are numb to it and accept it as a normal part of life. Common shock has numerous consequences, both psychologically and physiologically, beyond the event itself.

Weingarten reports that in New Orleans 91 percent of fifth graders report witnessing violence, such as shootings or stabbings. In Washington, D.C. 72 percent of fifth graders report witnessing similar events. Studies at Case Western Medical School found that young children (prior to age 2) exposed to violence have permanent neurological and brain chemistry change. Bessel van den Kolk, M.D. has found in his research that these children's brains can't discern between threatening and non-threatening stimuli in their environment.

Trauma response is not limited to witnessing violence. Weingarten found that witnessing illness can elicit a trauma-like response in family members and professional care givers. Researchers have also noted that trauma-type reactions may develop in response to medical procedures. Duke University studied the mental ability of coronary bypass patients for five years post surgery. Forty-two per cent of the patients in this study developed depression after surgery. A similar study at John Hopkins found depression in twelve per cent of the patients studied.

Post-traumatic stress response can manifest in different ways. Mark Lerner of the American Academy of Experts in Traumatic Stress lists a range of cognitive and emotional responses to trauma, such as: shock; highly anxious or stunned; emotional numbing; may feel as if "in a fog"; dissociation; dazed and apathetic; feelings of unreality; panic, fear, hopelessness, aloneness, emptiness, uncertainty, terror, horror, anger, hostility, irritability, depression, grief and feelings of guilt. They may experience impaired concentration and attention span: persevering thoughts of the traumatic event and hyper-vigilance.[3]

Many of these same emotions can also be attributed to cancer treatment outcomes. Helplessness, depression, and psychic distress are highly correlated to poor cancer treatment outcomes.[4] These emotional responses are also cited as suppressing immune system response which inhibits the body's natural defense against the growth of cancer cells.[6] In his research, Riley (1975) found that by varying stress he could alter the incidence of breast cancer in mice from ninety-two per cent in stressful conditions to seven per cent in a protected environment.[5] If traumatic stress and carcinogenic agents are contributing factors in the body's breakdown and inability to address cancer cells, then we must also consider that a war approach to cancer treatment may also be counterproductive.

SHAMANISM: The Original Trauma Medicine

An approach based in the traditions of shamanism offers a model for a healthier adaptation to life stressors than does a model of war and conflict. Shamanism is the oldest form of spiritual practice and healing known in human history. Anthropologists adapted the word "shaman" from the Tungus tribal word "saman" to describe a myriad of methods that medicine people throughout the world practice in common.

Mircea Eliade in his classic book, *Shamanism*, described the characteristics of a shaman as a man or woman who "journeys" in an altered state of consciousness, usually induced by rhythmic drumming or other repetitive sounds, such as chanting. In these journeys, the soul of the shaman travels through a cosmology to a place described as the lower world (a world described as beneath the surface of the earth), the middle world (a world which mirrors our familiar everyday world), and the upper world (a world above the sky). There the shaman senses and engages with compassionate and helpful spirits who guide and empower him/her in the work he or she does for the community. When someone becomes a shaman, it is often the result of that person being exposed to and healing from a profound trauma or a severe life-threatening illness. This is sometimes called the "shamanic crisis." Joan Halifax in *Shamanic Voices* explains this phenomenon.

"Those who have nearly died, through an accident or severe illness, or who have suffered a psychological or spiritual trauma of such proportions that they are catapulted into the territory of death will come to know the inner workings of crisis. The shaman learns to integrate the experiences of sickness, suffering, dying and death, as well as to share special knowledge of these powerful events with those who face disease or death for the first time."[6]

On the other hand, not everyone who has a significant trauma or illness has an experience that opens them up to the knowledge of the hidden world.

Traditionally people do not name themselves shamans. It is a distinction given by the community that has witnessed their healing gifts. It is also acknowledged that it is not the shaman's own power being used in healings, but rather that they are vessels for the power of Spirit working through them. These sacred healers have a responsibility to the spirits and to the community. The power is not theirs to own.

Jeanne Achterberg, Ph.D., a psychoneuroimmunology researcher, notes that in the field of psychology the phenomenon of dissociation (experiences where clients report witnessing themselves from outside their bodies as in childhood sexual abuse, Post Traumatic Stress Disorder (PTSD), the effects of anesthesia), is what shamans throughout the world call soul loss. Soul loss, from the view of shamans and folk healers, contributes to a range of illnesses including cancer.

Jeanne Achterberg further elaborates on this, adding:

"Soul loss is regarded as the gravest diagnosis in the shamanic nomenclature, being seen as a cause of illness and death. Yet it is not referred to at all in modern western medical books. Nevertheless, it is becoming increasingly clear that what the shaman refers to as soul loss—that is, injury to the inviolate core that is the essence of the person's being— does manifest in despair, immunological damage, and a host of other very serious disorders. It seems to follow the demise of relationship with loved ones, career, or other significant attachments."[7]

A shaman's trance has some similarities to the state of dissociation, so Achterberg, by way of analogy, describes the trance methods as a natural understanding of human response for survival. Her research found that the trance states shamans use, with the influence of drumming sounds, activates the amygdala and brain stem. The amygdala plays a significant role in processing trauma.

The amygdala is part of what is called the limbic system, also sometimes called the reptilian brain. In evolutionary terms, it is considered the oldest part of the brain that links emotions and fear to learning and memory. Two recent studies by Robert Schultz and Brian Pasley (2003) found that scary stimuli have a "back road" to the amygdala. This back road takes sensory information directly from the hypothalamus and bypasses the visual cortex, where information would be analyzed, enabling us to think before acting.

Bessel van der Kolk, a professor of psychiatry and PTSD researcher at Boston University Medical School, explains that people with PTSD often will go from stimulus to response without psychologically assessing the meaning of an event. This back road freezes trauma into a part of the brain that experiences rather than analyzes what is going on and is not easily accessible vis-à-vis normal talk therapy. Dr. Van der Kolk describes trauma response as "bimodal", in that PTSD sufferers react excessively to fear stimuli, have especially vivid memories, and have flashbacks of the original trauma. At the same time, they also exhibit psychic numbing, avoidance, and selective amnesia. He shares that PTSD sufferers try to compensate for their chronic hyper-arousal by avoiding stimuli reminiscent of their trauma, while still emotionally numbing out. When everything is perceived as dangerous the body operates as if everything is an invasion. When the immune system becomes stressed by its response to trauma its reaction is lessened, "numbed." It may be analogous that, in the case of cancer, the immune system begins to no longer recognize or respond to invasive cancerous cells.

As Achterberg's research points out, the shaman's trance activates the amygdala, so it's feasible that the shaman's methods of healing and journey imagery could be a naturalistic approach to processing trauma. We've discussed that trauma decreases the body's immune system response, which can make us more vulnerable to malignancy. Since shamanic methods activate the amygdala and affect the same area as trauma, they can be used to heal the source, and identify a potential trigger, of malignant growth. Indigenous people often use drumming, singing, dancing, and ceremony as natural methods of processing traumatic stress. Direct spiritual information and revelation can also be accessed using these methods, which further enhances health and healing.

Rather than go to war against illness, shamans have operated as mediators between the spirit world and the ordinary world we live in to resolve aspects of trauma than contribute to illness. A shaman's belief is that healing the landscape of a person's soul creates the conditions for the body's innate ability to heal itself. Part of each person's healing process, potentially, is to use shamanic journeying as a way to bring healing imagery to the area of the brain, the amygdala, which holds the frozen trauma images.

While it is true that exposure to environmental pollution, radiation, other Carcinogens, or trauma increases the risk of creating serious chronic illness, Not everyone exposed to them develops a health problem. Frequently, cancer cells do not go on to become malignancies because our body's own defense systems destroys the immature cancer cells before they become tumors. Within each of us lies the innate capacity to heal.

What are the predisposing factors within the soul of each person that contribute to illness? Achterberg, Simonton, and Mathews-Simonton (1976) said, "...it is reasonable to assume that people with certain psychological and behavioral traits would have weaknesses in specific target organs."[8] In certain shamanic traditions, each organ and part of the body contains an aspect of the soul. Soul is the immaterial essence of a person that bridges the spiritual and physical world. Soul connects us to the larger world and to our sense of purpose. Just like the uniqueness of fingerprints, each soul is different. We each bring our uniqueness to learn, to share our gifts, and to love. Each soul is shaped by events in one's life and by the meanings we give those events.

A theoretical model of how the soul embodies trauma can provide a road map for understanding illness in its spiritual form. The model explores commonly observed themes of how people respond to traumatic events in their lives. It looks at the meanings ascribed to the events and stories used to explain them. We each hold the stories of our own history and the history of the world around us in our minds and bodies. To heal from any illness requires looking at the larger terrain of the soul.

We all have various ways of responding and coping with traumatic events. Some of these responses can block the body's ability to process trauma, which can later become more vulnerable to illness. Some of the common ways of coping are:

1. We endure and try to withstand our suffering without collapsing or giving in.

2. We utilize denial and minimalization to unconsciously detach ourselves from emotion and the truth of the situation.

3. We try to bypass and deny our experience through telling ourselves we must transcend evil and traumatic events through spiritual beliefs. Consider, for example, the phrase, "We just need to give it to love and light." Attempting to not experience and live fully through challenging life events can become another form of detachment.

4.   We seek revenge. Neither burying nor rising above a situation, we seek to get even no matter what the cost to ourselves. From this view, we are constantly looking for something and someone to blame.

5.   We look for means of escape from the situation that overwhelms us. We may dissociate and leave our bodies. We may make ourselves so agreeable that we lack the form and everything just flows through us. We may find forms of addiction to help us escape, such as alcohol or other drugs.

When we embody these responses to traumatic events, we often block the experiences of our despair, fear, and grief. In doing so we may also block our ability to heal what is blocked or thwarted, creating a greater opening for ill-ness to form in the body. Our mind and soul try to ascribe meaning to these events so the internal distress can be tolerated.

Drawing from anecdotal observations of working with patients who have cancer, a number of common themes evolved around specific organs and areas of the body. Vulnerabilities in these areas of he body may manifest as a variety of illnesses, not just cancer. Later on there will be opportunities to work with this model directly.

CHART OF OBSERVED EMBODIED STORY POSSIBILITIES

Bone cancer—an expression of ancestral (family feeling of) inferiority, insecurity, and low self-worth passed on through generational conditioning. These feelings can extend back for many years.

Liver Cancer—fear of deprivation or not having enough. It may also be triggered by attack on one's power or life force by others who are envious.

Thyroid cancer—deep unexpressed feelings of powerlessness that may be triggered by trauma stories. Unable to give expression to the felt response to situations in one's life.

Lung Cancer—fear of suffocation. This suffocation may be literal or in relationships with others. A life without meaning suffocates the soul. Breath brings the power of the Creator into one's being and energizes the soul to express its larger purpose to the whole.

Kidney cancer—expression of not wanting to live at times in their lives and viewing the world as unfair. May manifest as kidney illness or high blood pressure.

Breast and Prostate cancers—conflicts with partners/others. May involve having to give nurturance when they didn't want to and reflect buried resentments.

Blood illnesses, like leukemia or platelet disorders—vulnerability (like a child) and reactive response to hypocrisy and untruthfulness by significant people in their lives. It may also emerge from being personally untruthful to others. Additionally, not living in accordance with their true nature may contribute to blood illnesses.

These stories, embodied in the soul, block the body's natural ability to heal itself. In the pain of separation, consciously or unconsciously, each of us seeks an explanation for our feelings and experiences. These explanatory stories and beliefs can either contribute to our illness or to our health.

Here are some examples from cases that have helped form the model described above:

A fifty-year old man had an aggressive form of prostate cancer that had spread into his bones. In interviewing him, he described himself as having given up on his desire to play music in order to care for his ill parents. Though he could admit his resentment, his outward affect was quite flat. Married with two young adult children, he had feelings of not being up to his wife's standards. His son was pursuing a dream of music and he described that relationship as close. He did a journey with me on the question of what his illness was trying to say to him. He met a fierce looking illness in the journey that said to him " I have no respect for your giving in, so I'm taking over." Afterwards, his own interpretation of this is, "My past choices have come back to haunt me." The next step in his work was self-forgiveness and learning how to move forward.

A 23-year old married woman with a young child was diagnosed with thyroid cancer. She felt disfigured by the size of her protruding tumor. As a young child she grew up in Belorussia and was exposed to radiation from the

Chernobyl nuclear reactor meltdown. Now living in a tiny one-bedroom apartment with her child, her husband and his mother, she felt overwhelmed by her mother-in-law's constant criticisms. Her husband ignored her pleas for help and often went out drinking. She attended school where she was studying psychology. She admitted to constant ruminations during her pregnancy, fearful that her child would be deformed. The baby is fully healthy. Soon due for thyroid surgery, she wondered if she would be healthy enough to meet her child's needs. In her journey to learn what her illness was teaching her, she was taken to a field near her family home in Belorussia. Lots of people, young and old, were wandering around aimlessly like zombies crying out "Why? Why?" Her own interpretation was that this was telling her what she already believed—that bad things happened to her because she was not a good person.

An eighty-six year old Holocaust survivor was originally found passed out by a dumpster and brought to the hospital. Upon waking, she was disoriented. Initial assessment found her to be malnourished. As she began to recover, it was discovered she had bone cancer. She was not fluent in English and spoke a mix of Yiddish and German. After coming to the United States in the post war years, she worked at a hotel in housekeeping. She had lost her only child in a horrific concentration camp incident. She maintained a lot of survivor behaviors, such as rummaging through garbage to find scraps of food or thrown out clothing. Throughout her life, she had horded every cent she could. Her family had always been poor and in her words, "looked down upon." In my journey for her, her illness told stories of her family and how they had been plagued by bad luck. For example, the illness told a story of her father, who apparently was quite bright at mathematics He was to go to college at a very young age, but family sickness forced him to go to work to support the family. In telling her what the illness reported, she said it was very true about her father. Soul retrieval helped her general anxiety subside and she appeared brighter. Care was arranged for her post hospitalization, and her main wish was to have chocolate every day, which was arranged.

A woman in her early 20's had a blood platelet disorder. She was given steroids as treatment and she wanted to get off them. She felt that she had something like fibromyalgia or chronic fatigue syndrome because of her symptoms of tiredness, headaches, and overall body weakness. Her journey to meet the spirit of her illness revealed a little sad girl as the illness. She was described as appearing to be five years old. The illness was filled with mistrust and did not want to talk much in the journey at first. The power animal helping in the journey was able to comfort the little girl who then shared her anger over being repeatedly punished by her father after her mother made up lies about her behavior. In this case, we did a series of soul retrievals and she continued her journeywork to build relationship with the illness. As she gained more and more trust with the illness, her symptoms began to subside and she was able to cut down on medications.

SHAMANIC HEALING METHODS WITH CANCER

A spiritual approach to healing starts with the question of "Who is the person who happens to have this illness?" This helps us understand that each person is unique and one size does not fit all. It allows the healer to remain curious and open hearted. While soul retrieval, extraction, power animal retrievals and other healing techniques of traditional shamanism can be used, the uniqueness of the person influences the specifics of the path taken. An aspect of shamanic healing traditions is to either put something back that has been lost, or to remove an illness which has been taken on.

Some brief definitions of healing methods are as follows:

Soul retrieval is the restoration of parts of the soul that have separated from the body in order to protect itself from harm. Most typically, the separation occurs as reaction to traumatic events in a person's life. People describe the loss of soul in many different ways. Common statements that reflect soul loss are: "I had a car accident and I jumped out of my skin." "I watched myself from a distance, while I was being abused." "I gave my soul away because I thought I was being loved." "It was like my body was there, but my mind was off somewhere else." In essence, soul retrieval reflects the commonality of dissociation as a natural means of self-protection.

Power animal retrieval seeks to restore lost vitality/energy in the form of a helping animal spirit that has been lost. We often give away our inner vitality and don't nurture our connection with Spirit. We also live in a culture that constantly attacks another's power through envy or criticism. Shamanic traditions believe that this can lead to the loss of our vitality.

Extraction is a healing method shamans use to remove spiritual Intrusions, or what they sometimes call a "spiritual virus." There is a belief that intentionally directed negativity towards others or oneself creates spiritual illness that if not removed can lead to physical illness. Many shamanic traditions also believe that the disembodied dead, souls that have not crossed over after death, can also attach themselves to the living and cause illness. Shamans work to bring healing to the dead so they can transition to the other world.

Much of what shamans do is identify the spiritual context that supports the development of disease. There are a number of methods to divine a spiritual diagnosis. These divinations guide the shamans in healing the spiritual aspect of disease, which may or may not bring about a physical change. The knowledge gained from divining with spirits directs how the shamans approach the problems presented. The shamans then offer themselves, on behalf of their patients, as vessels for the healing power of the spirits.

In the coming chapters, you'll learn some of the specifics involved in spiritual healing work with cancer. Breaking it down into a variety of topics will provide a deeper understanding into the issues involved and the approaches used to promote healing. Each segment will include teachings about shamanic journeying that will help you better understand and heal aspects of your illness. Rather than have treatment be something that happens to you, these experiential journeys allow you to fully participate in your own healing. The structure of the journeys and exercises are designed to assist in the prevention of spiritual illness.

CHAPTER 3

What You Give Life: The Journey Begins

"One can't believe impossible things," Alice said. "I dare say you haven't had much practice," said the Queen..." Why sometimes I've believed as many as six impossible things before breakfast."—Lewis Caroll, Through the Looking Glass

"Yet, while science attempts to describe nature and to distinguish between dream and reality, it should not be forgotten that human beings call as much for dream as for reality. It is hope that gives life a meaning. And hope is based on the prospect of being able to turn the actual world into a possible one that looks better. When the French writer, Tristan Bernard was arrested with his wife by the Gestapo, he told her, "The time of fear is over. Now comes the time of hope."—Francois Jacob, The Possible and the Actual

When I was eight years old, I had a dream where a tree talked to me and said, "You are my brother. You are to come find me and bring me to your home where we will grow old together." That next morning when I woke up,

I was determined to find that tree.

I made two peanut butter and jelly sandwiches and filled my father's old World War II canteen with water. Then finding a shovel, I trekked on my adventure to find this tree. It was a hot and humid August day when I began my search. As I wandered through fields of what was once a wetlands, I eventually heard a soft whisper in the wind calling, "I'm over here, I'm over here!"

As I turned and looked, there stood a tree much taller than I. Inside I glowed with joy upon meeting my brother, the tree. And so I began to dig and dig, deep into the earth. I was meticulous with the shovel and my hands, being careful to not hurt the tree roots. All the while I worked, dripping wet from the toil of my efforts, the tree sang a song with the wind that urged me on.

The hours went by and the sun was lowering on the horizon. My anxiety rose, for time was of the essence. In my family there were few rules. Yet the biggest crime, ranked even higher than murder one, was not being at the dinner table when my father got home from work. But I kept digging. Eventually the tree then said to me, "Chop my roots." I did as I was ordered and then began to drag this large tree home. Once home, I immediately dug a hole in the back yard and planted the tree.

My parents, looking out the back door, quietly shook their heads as if to say, "What has he done now?" Not a word was said. That night I had trouble sleeping, wondering about the tree. In the early morning hours, I walked out to check on the tree and in my mind I could hear him moaning, "I don't feel good." Instantaneously, I could feel the dread filling my soul. If this was my brother and we were to "grow old together", then the future didn't look very good.

From that point on, I would sneak out of the house after my parents went to sleep. With an old army blanket and a pillow, I would wrap myself around the tree and pray to God for my brother's life. All the while, I knew I was praying for my own life as well. As the days went on, the tree's leaves began to fall off and some limbs were clearly dead. My fear was rising and the nightly prayers became tearful pleas to the heavens. A child's mind wasn't processing the coming of autumn as part of nature's cycle of death and re-birth. After each night of holding the tree and praying, I would sneak back into the house in the early light of morning before the sunrise.

One night, my father found me wrapped around the tree. "What are you doing out here?" I cried as I told my father the story of my dream and how the tree was dying. He listened quietly and then got up and walked away. A few minutes later he came back out with a knife, drug a water hose to the tree, cut off a small piece of dead branch and ground it up at the base of the tree. My father was an older man, who had war injuries to his knees, so I was amazed as he began to dance and sing around the tree. I had never seen him do anything like this before or since. After several minutes of dancing, he poured water onto the tree. Finally he looked at me and said, "What you give love, you give life." My father never spoke again of that night. Through the years, I've come to appreciate the lesson my father taught: The lesson of intention. Just as the tree cried out for my love and eventually grew strong and healthy, many children cry out for attention and love. The example that comes to mind is that of a young child at a swimming pool yelling to mom or dad, "Watch this" as they would run and jump into the pool. And the typical good parent smiles and says, "Great jump, sweetie." That ritual might go on a hundred times, with each jump being witnessed and smiled upon.

Another strong example that demonstrates the power of intention is an old Jewish story about a man who is very sick with cancer and goes to his doctor. The doctor says to the man, " Let me explain something to you, in this room there are three of us—you, your disease, and me. If you and I join forces, then we'll outnumber the disease two-to-one, and we have a good chance of winning. But, if you join forces with the disease, there is not much I can do."

HEALING PRINCIPLE OF ATTENTION AND INTENTION

"Energy tends to go where there is the most excitement, most clarity, most intensity. Energy follows attention."—Wendy Palmer, American Aikido Teacher, author of *The Intuitive Body*

These stories raise the question of where we put our attention when confronting a diagnosis of cancer. Certainly anyone with a life threatening disease can tell you how many times they tell their story over and over to various health professionals, family members, and friends. The number of times a person talks about their illness isn't what gives it power, but rather the story they carry about it. If our story about our illness has few possible outcomes and many obstacles, then it's more likely things will head in a negative direction. If our stories are more like a river that creatively flows in many different directions with many possible outcomes, then the healing possibilities increase.

There is a simple but powerful way to demonstrate these ideas by utilizing concepts from aikido. Aikido, a Japanese martial arts form, means "way of harmony." Standing on your feet, put your hands on your belly about two inches below your belly button. This place is called "center". Take some deep breathes into your hands and focus the attention of your mind to this place. Ask someone to place a hand on your shoulder as you're doing this. When you sense you are able to bring all of your attention to the spot just below your belly button, have your partner gradually increase the pressure and notice the solidness you experience. In aikido, when a person is connected to center, he is connected to the earth and to the sky. Once you have achieved a place of center and feel solid, think about your cancer.

Notice what happens. As your attention shifts from your center and connects to the problem, you lose balance easily. Now bring your attention back to the place where your hands are below your belly button to re-center yourself.

It's easy to be pulled into identifying with your disease. While this is meant to be an analogy to the idea that what we give attention to we give life, it doesn't address the issue of alliance in healing. In the model of this book, the key alliance is one's relationship with Spirit. One could easily substitute the word Creator or God here. For many tribal people, there is recognition that when one is sick it is important for the community to gather in healing support. The sickness of one is viewed as a threat to the health of the whole.

HEALING REQUIRES RELATIONSHIP WITH HELPING SPIRITS

There are many reasons why babies cry when they are born, and one of them is the sudden separation from the world of pure dreams, where all things are made of enchantment, and where there is no suffering.
—Ben Okri, *The Famished Road*

The despair of facing cancer expresses itself spiritually as dispiritedness. To be dispirited calls many to question their relationship to the Creator/God. Dispiritedness is separation and disconnection from our spiritual knowing. It manifests as a loss of vitality and sense of meaning. Shamans work to restore us to the "world of pure dreams" through power animals and soul retrieval.

C.S. Lewis wrote *A Grief Observed* as a way of not losing his faith in God after his wife died of cancer, and he was fighting his own dispiritedness in the aftermath of her death. As he reminds us:

One never meets just Cancer, or War, or Unhappiness (or Happiness). One only meets each hour or moment that comes. All manner of ups and downs. Many bad spots in our best times, many good ones in our worst. One never gets the total impact of what we call "the thing itself." But we call it wrongly. The thing itself is simply all those ups and downs: the rest is a name or an idea.[1]

In his struggle, C.S. Lewis was not afraid of losing his belief in God, but rather that he would become disillusioned with the ways of God. Numerous cancer survivors have cited that spiritual practice was essential to their healing and survival from cancer. Engaging the healing spirits and being able to wrestle with one's own dispiritedness becomes a means for cancer patients to empower themselves in their own healing journey.

Shamanic journeying is a method used to go into trance and connect with healing power and wisdom of the spirits. It is a form of active and living prayer. In most cases, repetitive drumming or chanting is used to induce a receptive state of trance to connect spiritually. When we enter this state of consciousness, we are moving from the dream of the reality of cancer, or any other life-threatening disease, to the dream of possibility and hope.

When one is listening to repetitive drumming it induces the brain to go into theta brain waves. When the brain is in theta, our minds address questions and problems in a much different way than our ordinary, linear ways of thinking. The mind in theta thinks and understands in patterns of relationship. It puts together new and creative solutions to the problem instead of relying on an old pattern of response which may or may not be working . Additionally, once in this state of trance, receptivity to spiritual knowledge and power increases. When a shaman says the drum is the heartbeat of the earth, the words reflect the understanding of relationship for the resonance of the drum and the resonance of the earth are similar.

The most important aspect to using the journeying method is intention. Intention brings us to a place of clarity and strength. When we go crooked with our intention, meaning that we are either half-hearted about what we are seeking, or our intention is simply not true in our core being, our physical and emotional energy goes flat and we get distracted.

Working with one's own spiritual helpers leads to walking the "wisdom trail." Affirming one's wisdom and quest for spiritual learning helps cancer patients focus on what they can do to overcome the traps of negativity. The relationship with spirit diminishes the profound sense of aloneness many cancer patients will report. It also offers empowerment in the journey toward healing. If you find you're distracted or you have difficulty staying present, don't be too hard on yourself as they are both common responses to dealing with trauma.

In some ways the question is, "What is important enough to you that it keeps you here?" There is one patient; I'll call Ruth, whose health issues made being alive seem impossible to her. Her heart muscle was extremely weak. Cancer had spread throughout her body. Physicians told her there was little, if anything, they could do. Yet in the time I knew her, she always had one more event she wanted to attend. Each time just before such an event, she would look like she wasn't going to make it, yet miraculously she would rally enough to leave her care facility and attend the family gathering. What keeps you going in your life?

Throughout this book you will be given questions you can use to help in determining your intention as you journey for your healing. These questions can also be used for personal reflection and exploration. When shamans enter the journey trance; they travel to different places in their spiritual imagination. You will be given directions for accessing helping spirits from two different places within the shaman's cosmology; what shamans refer to as the upper and lower worlds.

Let's begin with basic descriptions and suggestions for two beginning approaches to working with helping spirits. These will allow you to practice prior to working with the later exercises in the book.

JOURNEY TO THE LOWER WORLD

Find a dark and quiet space to relax and get receptive. You may find it helpful to use a bandana to help blindfold your eyes to help you with your spiritual journeying. Close your eyes and begin to focus on an opening in the earth that you will want to enter in your imagination. Most find it helpful to imagine something that is familiar to you. It can be a cave or an animal hole.

It can be a hole in a tree or the water springs coming up from the earth. Spend time connecting with this place in your mind.

In each journey, you will have an intention. In this journey you will be seeking to go to a world beneath the surface of the earth to meet a helping animal spirit. Throughout the journey you will want to remind yourself of your intention as it helps you maintain focus and helps keep your mind from wandering. When you meet this helping animal spirit, you will ask it to help you feel stronger and more alive. In each journey you do, you'll go with one question and one question only so you know the information you receive is giving answer to that question. Often the journey information is given to the journeyer in symbolic form and having one question makes it easier to understand what this information is addressing. Remember that any time our mind wanders or you get caught up in internal dialogue about whether you are doing it right, repeat your intention—"I am going to the lower world to meet a helping animal spirit and ask for help in feeling stronger and more alive."

It helps to take time in the beginning to visualize your entry point and repeat your intention. You'll want to have shamanic drumming with callback beat either in your mp3 or iPod or stereo system. Let yourself feel the drumming and how it influences you. Enter your entrance point into the earth and begin to go down a tunnel. Allow the time you need to go down the tunnel. You have all the time you need to get there and explore the vastness. You are entering a state where time is suspended and all is possible. Once you see a light at the end of the tunnel and exit, begin to look for a helping animal spirit. Any animal you see, simply ask, "Are you my helping animal spirit?" In some way, directly or indirectly, you will get an answer. If it's "no" then move on until you meet the animal that is working with you. When you meet the animal helper, let it know you are there to ask for help in feeling stronger and alive. From that point on anything that happens in the journey will be your spiritual answer to the question, so pay careful attention to the setting and to everything that occurs.

At some point, the drumming will change to signal and end to the journey. When that happens, return in a conscious way the same way you entered the lower world. Before leaving, thank the helping spirit(s) for the help you received. If it feels right, ask what you can do in return to help the spirits. Right relationship requires a sense of honor and respect, and is reciprocal in nature. Remember to return up the tunnel to the entry point where you started. Once back in this realm, take time to reflect on your experiences. Keep a journal of your experiences. Don't be discouraged if it didn't seem successful the first time. Every spiritual approach requires practice and mastery. For the few days following your journey simply notice what lingering effects it seems to have on you.

HARMONY AND RESONANCE WITH CANCER

A World War II veteran in the hospital with cancer tells his physician in the days leading up to the invasion of Iraq by Post 9/11 America that "We should never go to war. War doesn't solve anything. We should always try to negotiate." He tells the physician that during the war he had appendicitis. "I am lying there in pain at the hospital. I heard lots of screams around me. Many of the screams were from German soldiers who had been shot. Those German soldiers were in just as much pain as I was."

Cancer emerges when our bodies are not in balance and harmony. Under these circumstances early cancer cells are not resolved through apoptosis (programmed cell death) or through normal immune system response. Like the story of the veteran, we are asked to consider another way of responding to crisis. While cancer presents itself as the body at war with itself, healing requires negotiation. Negotiation in this case is an attempt to establish relationship and resonance in order to influence a positive outcome.

As a young child, I was diagnosed with severe hearing loss. I began to learn how to lip read and talk with the aid of a speech therapist. In those early days the therapist would put one of my hands on her throat and place the other hand on my throat. The goal was to match the resonance of her making a sound with the resonance of my making the same sound. Though I was only a child of six I noticed that when the resonances matched, a feeling of peace would fill my being.

My great aunt Soshie would often ask me when we visited her, "what did you learn this week?" I told her about how I was learning to talk and the feelings in my hands. She had me do it with her. She said to me at the time, "When you and I make the same vibration it is healing. The body makes different sounds and you can heal in this way."

Valerie Hunt, a UCLA physiology professor and researcher, found in her research that the body makes different resonances/sounds. When the body is stressed and traumatized it generally responds in one of two ways. It either under responds (constricting) i.e., begins to shut down or it gets reactive and vigilant. Either response can correspond to illness in the body, but it has been generally observed that many cancers resonate in the under-responding range.

A common use of these concepts in healing work involves journeying to spirit helpers to learn the song of an illness. While in the journey state, the healer with the aid of his spirit helpers sings the song of the illness directly into the body, cupping one's hands over the area of the body to help hold the resonance of the song. As harmony between the illness and healer develops, the healer is taught by Spirit a healing sound and transitions into this new sound. This method has proven to help alleviate some of the pain certain cancer patients report.

For example, here is a sample case:

Ellen is a hospice patient whose cancer has spread throughout her body. She is literally being eaten up from the inside out. Though she receives prn morphine for pain, she is in constant pain. Singing over areas of pain in her body since she can not tolerate touch, her breathing slows to the song and it is easy to watch her body visibly relax to the song. She begins to cry as the pain dissipates. When I asked her afterwards why she was crying, she re-ported that the song reminded her of songs she hummed to her babies when they were young. She went on to say that she felt a lightness come into her and that in her mind she saw departed loved ones who told her they were waiting for her. She described this experience as filling up in love.

Matching resonance works to create harmony with the cancer. It is not an act of war, but rather a befriending and softening. In other words, a healing song can influence a different resonance. Sometimes the sound or song be-comes an ongoing chant for the patient, which creates a sense of comfort or acts as a palliative for the pain.

Helen is a former English literature professor who has retired early because of her long history of struggling with cancer. What began as breast cancer spread throughout her body. Her pain was great. As I matched the sound of the illness in her body it began to change into a soulful lamentation, and I saw the color in her face brighten as her breathing slowed to a deepening rhythm. When we were done, she said she felt as if the sounds reached a place deep inside her. She then recited these lines from the poem *Moving Forward* by Rainer Marie Rilke:

> "The deep parts of my life pour upward,
> as if the river shores were opening out.
> It seems that things are more like me now,
> that I can see farther into paintings.
> I feel closer to what language can't reach."

In her own beautiful way, Helen taught me how harmony worked in her.

Journey suggestion for the reader: Journey to your power animal with the intent of learning a healing song or sound. When you meet your power animal in the journey, ask it to teach you this song/sound and sing with it until you learn the song. Upon returning from the journey continue to sing the song throughout the day and notice how it affects you. If you have a circle of support, teach the song to them and ask them to form a circle around you and sing with you. Notice how the circle of resonance feels inside you, in those places that language can't reach.

_____

_____

_____

_____

_____

_____

_____

_____

_____

_____

_____

_____

THE RELATIONAL FIELD AS CONTEXT

When shamans look at cancer or any other illness, they are looking for the context that allows the disease to make sense. Each of us is in constant relationship to spiritual forces around us. We influence and are influenced by the spiritual field we are in contact with. Fields are invisible to our normal modes of perception, yet our senses are constantly aware of them.

Think of times when you went to work or school or visited the hospital. You might have said to yourself in some way, "It feels jittery here today". Maybe you got a queasy feeling in your stomach and wondered what was going on.

When there is disharmony in the field we sense it and it effects us in some palpably negative way. As a result, we get out of balance and harmony. The ways we are affected may be directing us to the type of spiritual healing that needs to occur.

It is equally true that within that field are healing influences as well. The air, the plants, the earth, the animals, the water, the ancestors; each person's helping spirits, and the place itself holds a resource of healing for each of us. Think of places you have been in your life that you associate with feeling happy or energized.

Arnold Mindell, founder of process-oriented psychotherapy, says:

'Fields may be invisible to the naked eye, yet they appear in the dreams of individuals, in the stories people tell about their groups, and even in the myths of nations. Individuals and groups are the battleground for the characters in the myths to complete their mystical conflicts. It is this dreamlike nature of fields that makes it so difficult for ecologists, economists, and politicians to deal with the world, because it is only partly organized by causal influences. The world is also organized by non-causal influences, by the dreaming field, and we need to be shamans and visionaries as well as politicians and scientists to solve world problems.[2]

Everything touched by a field becomes part of it. To shamans, the spiritual-field crosses time and space and exists whether we are in contact with it at that moment or not. Fields have no boundaries. A field is a flowing thing. It flows within itself. It flows from one place to another. Attractors in our human field, like our traumas, will attract things to the field that mimic it and are toxic to it.

Each of us is as much like a field as we are bodies. Each of us is made up as much by our thoughts, ideas, feelings and dreams as we are physical matter. As spiritual beings there is no separation internally or externally in the spiritual fields. Our own personal history and the history within the field become one.

Cancer has its own complexities, in part because it develops over many years. Cancer has history. Our souls have touched and been touched in a myriad of ways and forces. Spiritually we have all become a tapestry of histories interwoven into the fabric of our being. We notice the tapestry of history when we are ill. Understanding the field influences that are occurring provides a context for understanding disease.

An example of field influences in cancer follows below:

A couple of people come for healing who worked at a cancer pain treatment clinic within a larger teaching hospital setting. Within the previous year, six out of eleven staff members had been diagnosed with a variety of cancers. The staff members were concerned that cancer had become contagious. The spiritual dreaming (journeying) for these people who had come for healing unbeknownst to each other revealed the place had become sick from what had been brought to that place and not cleared. When asked why they thought staff members were getting sick, their answers focused on the idea that the stress of the work had made them all vulnerable to what the various patients carried in them. When I journeyed on behalf of the staff members, a dark filmy water with flames presented itself as a hungry and angry presence wanting to be fed. According to my spirit helpers it was the illness that had been brought here by an earlier patient and that had stayed on, jumping from person to person. A healing ritual was done to take the dark water and fire presence to a nearby lake to neutralize its effect.

In this case, the sickness of the people coming to the clinic was influencing the spiritual field. Each person who visited the clinic brought his or her entire histories with them. Spiritually it is important to not only work to bring healing to the person, but also the larger terrain of field influences which continue to exist beyond each person's illness. While hospitals work hard to establish sterile environments, traditional healers work to maintain balance and harmony in the place itself.

MOVING FROM WAR TO PEACE WITH CANCER

"Enter this dark night of the soul, insists the voice of despair. Look at the world's pain without your usual protections. Descend to this place of near annihilation. If you can bear your way through this night with patience, you

will be moved in a muscular faith that has looked into the heart of darkness and emerged to affirm life."— Miriam Greenspan, *Healing through the Dark Emotions*

Most of us, when attacked will in some way either fight back or try to defend ourselves. To quote the World War II veteran mentioned earlier, "War never solves anything." True there are times when you have to send in the peacekeeping troops to level the playing field. As analogy, utilizing the best approaches of allopathic-trained physicians (oncologists) such as diagnoses, surgery, chemotherapy, and radiation are the peacekeeping techniques that level the playing field. Peace building seeks to heal the underlying conditions in the terrain of the soul so there is no further reoccurrence of the body going to war with itself (cancer). Peace building might include lifestyle changes such as diet, use of dietary supplements, and exercise as well as personal healing, spiritual practice, creating a community of support, and using rituals to bring balance and harmony to one's life.

It is understandable that we would go to war with cancer. In certain cases our lives are at stake. The cancer breaks off from a territory within the body. It sends off scout cells to establish new colonies and conquer new territories. As the body responds to defend itself, the cancer uses the response to feed itself and becomes stronger. Medicines attempt to cut off supply lines to the cancer cells they feed on. In certain cases, the cancer can form barriers that prevent intervention. Just as war can leave its mark on the landscape, cancer treatments can leave scars or numbness in areas of the body.

There are six principles essential to utilizing a spiritual based peace approach. These are:

Bringing peace to an illness requires being able to encounter and step into the experience of the illness.

Peace and healing require working from a place of non-agenda and non-attachment to outcome.

All feelings and emotions must be expressed. Emotions can be expressed through art, movement, or sounding.

Cultivating compassion, empathy, forgiveness, and gratitude are essential attitudes for healing.

Working in alliance with Spirit can transform swords of war (medicine) into plowshares of healing.

Healing requires moving from the symptoms to healing the undercurrent stories in the soul's terrain contributing to illness.

To bring peace to any illness, one must fully know the illness spiritually. They must work with their spirit helpers to meet the illness, learn about what its needs are and what it is trying to teach us. To fully know an illness may require filling up/merging with spiritual power in order to spiritually walk in the shoes of that illness. For example:

A girl in her late teens is with her mother to seek healing for a cancerous brain tumor that is inoperable. The girl and her mother have been told by the oncologist there is nothing that can be done. The girl is too weak to journey for herself, so a journey is done for her. The cancer presents itself like a small furry animal with fierce looking teeth. The animal tells me it is teaching self-defense. The journeyer's spirit helpers suggest merging with the cancer. The journeyer fills up in spiritual power and then steps into the illness as if putting on clothing. Inside the illness everything feels like attack, something akin to feeling vigilant. The journeyer jumps around as the illness in a dance that looks like dodge ball maneuvers. Upon the return from the journey, the girl is laughing as she said the illness looked silly. Her general mood and energy level showed improvement in the coming weeks.

Once the spirit of the illness is more fully understood, it creates direction for further response. Patients may continue to dialogue with the illness to help dissipate its power over them. They may create rituals or daily lifestyle behavioral changes based on the information gained.

Dr. Keith Block, an integrative medicine oncologist cites that, "scientists found that restricting the expression of difficult emotions was actually associated with shorter survival"[3] in breast cancer patients. There are a number of tribal societies that utilize rituals to encourage expression as an aspect of peacemaking. An example of this is the Wayamous ceremony of the Yanomami, where the community bangs on the walls of the ceremonial lodge encouraging aggrieved parties to express emotions. As is the case in many of these types of rituals, there is a time when a person in expressing intense emotions begins to lose attachment to them and may laugh, for example, at how silly they are. The ritualization of expression and the support of community can be helpful for some cancer patients. At the same time, denial can be a positive fighting aspect for certain cancer patients. In other words, expressing feelings for the sake of expressing emotions isn't necessarily healing. The key is in the expression and in the moving towards compassion and understanding. An example case of this follows:

Scott is a middle-aged man diagnosed with an aggressive form of prostate cancer that has spread to his bones. Through his whole life he had tried to be a "good person," yet often found himself privately being angry and resentful. In his own journeying, the spirits kept showing him that the illness was the anger literally eating away at him. He felt blocked from feeling and from expressing his feelings. With encouragement, he brought together a circle of friends to drum and encourage him in a fire ceremony. He danced around the fire symbolically throwing his anger into the fire while the circle drummed for him. Additionally, they yelled and screamed encouraging him to get into the releasing dance and his vocalization. He began to yell at the fire and utilized the ritual energy to support his expression. Afterwards, he reported a feeling of deep peace that was new for him. While the cancer did not subside, he lived vitally for a couple more years which was well beyond the expected outcome given his cancer's progression.

In this process there is no attempt to affect a specific outcome. The healer simply focuses on bringing a spiritual influence to the process. It is, in essence, an act of surrender to what Spirit brings. A core belief is that a relationship with the illness brings more influence and change than trying to deny its existence. When there is no agenda, the illness softens and is more easily engaged in the larger story, removing the barriers to healing. Healing seeks to restore balance and harmony, which may or may not affect a cure. Living beyond the determined timeline with vitality and purpose is just as much a sign of healing as spontaneous remission. An example of non-attachment to outcome follows:

Michael is a late 30's gay male with AIDS. He has Karposi's sarcoma. A very kind and community active man, he had built up a successful business. He came for healing with the expressed attitude that he just wanted to die, but his life partner insisted that he come for healing. His partner wanted a miracle. Michael had become increasingly isolated as his sickness progressed. The healing work became a journey to restore lost soul parts from his childhood. Soul loss is often associated with illness of the immune system so it was not a surprising session. After blowing in the soul parts, a song was sung to his soul and Michael began to weep. "I feel love, I feel love, " was what he kept saying over and over. He shared that he had never felt loved in his whole life. In the weeks ahead, he found peace. He was able to share this new love with his partner and die gracefully surrounded by a circle of friends.

Michael's internal life was rife with self-recrimination. He had rarely shared his internal struggles with others. There is a range of response one can have to a life-threatening illness including anger, despair, denial, grief, fear, anguish, and numbing. Given the relationship of trauma to the development of cancer, it is not surprising to see a number of cancer patients respond to the news of cancer as if they have been traumatized again.

Like Michael, a large number of patients seen for healing work carry a long history of self-recrimination. From the viewpoint of shamans, this negativity and attack of self is a form of spiritual illness that must be extracted. If carrying traumatic events from earlier in their lives, it is not uncommon to hold oneself to blame for what occurred. Developing compassion, forgiveness, and gratitude restores vitality and life force. It gives patients what they need to cultivate a fighting spirit as they embrace a path of healing. For example:

Hanna is an early-sixties Jewish woman with a long history of depression and passivity. She has never been known to have much energy. As she learns her breast cancer has spread to her lymph nodes; she remains emotionally flat and outwardly noncommittal. Her religion is important to her and she seeks healing with a Jewish viewpoint. A soul retrieval is done which indicates a domineering mother and a passive father. So overwhelmed by her mother, she had given up some early life dreams in order to keep her mother at bay. She had wanted to study medicine and become a physician. In a subsequent journey, she was given a song titled "its never too late", which she was guided to sing. It was difficult to get her to let it out but with a lot of prodding the volume and resonance of the song increased. We went to a nearby lake where I encouraged her to give herself forgiveness for putting her dreams aside and to make offerings to God as gratitude for having a chance to prove that it's never too late. After the ritual, I insisted that she study medicine on her own behalf and learn all she could about her disease. A few weeks later she came in to tell me what she had learned in her studies and that she had gone into remission. She was smiling and bright.

Hanna had moved out of a story that had ruled her life. A story of hiding her own dreams to avoid the critical wrath of her mother. In her own healing journey, she was able to create a story of "it's never too late" which opened numerous possibilities for her. Additionally, she had reframed her chemotherapy and radiation treatments into sweetness and sunshine, which she believed lessened the side effects of her treatments. Hanna was especially proud of the fact that she had not lost her hair. There have been numerous cases in which the spiritual approach of asking that the medical treatments go exactly to where they are needed most has successfully softened the effects of the treatments.

HEALING AND CEREMONIES

"The ceremonial circle is the most effective form of breathing new life into the soul and spirit of human interchange, for inspiring renewed personal vision, and for recreating a cohesive community."—Sedonia Cahill and Joshua Halpern, *The Ceremonial Circle*

Creating a ceremony is a little bit like building a baseball field in the middle of an Iowa cornfield. Entering into our own field of dreams, we invoke the help of the spirits to a place and ask for their help. In a translation from a phrase in the Bible (Exodus), "build an altar of earth and I will dwell amongst you." Ceremony brings the power of the Creator to a place. It also brings the power of community and community support on behalf of the person who is ill. Many shamanic traditions hold that when one is sick, we are all sick. It is in our own best interest to support and help each other.

Numerous public health studies consistently show the one variable that predicts the best possible outcomes for major health concerns is the quality of community support a patient has. In The Healing Web: Social Networks and Human Survival by Marc Pilisuk, he points out what tribal people have known through the millennia—that our survival is linked in our connections with each other. Ceremony serves the purpose of bringing us together in the common intent of helping one to help the whole. Throughout my years of working with people diagnosed with cancer, I have developed a number of ceremonies, using the guidance provided in shamanic journeys.

As mentioned before, journeying is a form of spiritual learning; learning by doing; learning that cannot be successfully implemented merely by reading about ceremony in a book. For example, learning how to hold the space; keep the spiritual energy contained and active, requires sensitivity and skill. It is about understanding and containing the group resonance that builds during the ceremony, while staying connected to one's own spirit helpers. One must also understand sacred timing, and know when to shift the energy to a higher level. Equally important is a sense of knowing the right time to intervene. It is only through an evolving relationship with Spirit and direct hands-on experience that one can truly develop these gifts.

Healing work always varies case by case. In working with life-threatening illnesses, the best results are often within the context of a community circle with several healers involved. The model given to the author by his spirit helpers has a number of variations that have been used with success. There are two most common versions that spiritual guidance has directed.

In one version, a healer journeys to fill up with power by merging with his or her power animal and going to meet the spirit of the patient's cancer. Merging with one's own spirit helpers provides protection to the healer so they do not take on the illness. The healer learns the spirit of the illness's dance and then dances the spirit of the person's cancer. Another healer journeys to merge with his or her power animal and asks to learn the dance of healing, which he or she then dances. The outer circle of community support is drumming and focusing its attention on the person who is dancing the healing. The patient is also watching this dancer so they can learn this dance of the healing. Meanwhile, everyone ignores the healer who is dancing the spirit of cancer. The spirit of the cancer may yell, scream, try to get into the faces of people sitting in circle. Like cancer, it needs to be fed to stay alive and will do all it can to maintain its sense of life. As the cancer spirit loses power, this dancer leaves the circle and disengages from the illness. More people are brought into the circle to learn the dance of healing and build its power. The patient watches, and if able, eventually joins the dance. If they learn the dance, it is prescribed that they do the dance as living prayer every day of their recovery.

Here is a case example:

Terry is a diabetic man who has cancer in his leg. Surgery is done to remove the cancer, but due to his diabetes the incisions are not healing. The dancers begin to dance. The dancer of illness is moving around in a zombie like way dragging the leg that has had surgery. The dancer who is dancing the dance of healing is flowing around the room in a fluid manner using her hands as if she were waving veils. As the dancer of illness leaves the circle, Terry jumps up and looks at his leg. Once the ceremony ends, he pulls up his pant leg and removes the bandages. He reports feeling tingling and heat running through his leg during the dance. Upon examination, he is shocked to see that the incisions have healed completely and the color of his skin is normal.

The other ceremony involves healers taking on four different roles. One journeys on what might be a creative intervention. He or she goes to his or her helping spirits to get a healing story or poem, an image of art to draw or sculpt, or some other form of creativity that brings healing to the patient. These interventions are often extremely symbolic and in many cases the symbols have special meaning to the patients themselves. A second journeyer operates in the traditional shamanic healer role and does whatever healing the spirits direct such as soul retrieval and extraction. A third journeyer asks the spirits how to bring in a disruptive power that can break through the spiritual blocks that are contributing to the disease or preventing the healing from taking place. They might yell, scream, drum loudly, sing loudly, or dance fiercely to accomplish this. They are raising the power needed to keep the river of healing flowing. The last journeyer works with the spirits to send unconditional love to the patient as love is the strongest healing force. Often this person has merged with an aspect of the Divine and is toning while sending energy through their hands.

Here is a case example:

Donna, a middle aged woman comes to a shamanism workshop to check out whether this is a direction she wants to go in her healing. During a break, she approaches me to tell of the many tumors she has throughout her body. She was going to have surgery that week. Her prognosis was not good and she had only agreed to her surgery because the doctors said it would remove some difficult tumors and extend her quality of life. She asked if a healing ceremony could be done for her in the workshop. During the ceremony, the person journeying for creativity whispers a story they received in a journey to Donna while the drumming and other work is occurring.

"Once you were a river and it flowed everywhere. All life was supported by you and the land was lush and green. But one day things changed and you became a road, but in your soul you were a river. As a road you became very hungry and you wanted to eat and eat and eat. But the river that brought the lushness was no more and the food disappeared."

"One day an ant came and began to eat the road and each bite released water. To the ant, the road was very juicy. Other ants came as they heard of the juiciness and the road slowly but surely became a droplet of water, then a puddle, then a creek, and then a river."

The provocateur was jumping and yelling all around her. "Let Me In! Let Me In!" The one bringing in unconditional love, loved. And the shamanic healer did extraction and soul retrieval. When it was all over, Donna reported, "Nothing happened. I felt nothing." She was told that we weren't attached to the outcome, yet had faith that the spirits work in whatever way they do and encouraged patience.

A year later, she came to another workshop. She shared that when she went to see her doctor for the pre-surgery physical she told her doctor about the ceremony. In further examination, they found her cancer had gone into full remission. There were no tumors to be found. It has been found in several cases of healing that the patients who report feeling nothing have been the ones with the strongest results.

Arthur Egendorf paraphrasing Ralph Waldo Emerson in his book about veterans healing from the Vietnam war said, "Spirit is nothing to hold onto. We are always losing it and always having to regain it." In working with cancer patients, there comes a point where what they lost in becoming sick, or what they had, is no longer adequate for the challenges they face. Time after time, in the exploration of what is "missing" it isn't always that they lost something of themselves. More often than not, they discover they never had it. They are seeking something they have never experienced or known. In their moment of vulnerability, facing the prospect of life and death head on, they are given the great task of discovering what is sacred in that moment. They must learn how to restore their relationship with Spirit in a way that is healing not only for themselves but also for those around them. Ultimately, it is the heart and commitment to the task at hand that enable patient, healers, and community to become vessels of the Spirit and bring healing.

CHAPTER 4

Transforming Despair and War with Cancer Through Spiritual Healing and Learning

"We are not unified, we often
feel that we are, because we do not have many bodies and many limbs,
and because one hand doesn't usually hit the other. But, metaphorically,
that is what happens within us."—Roberto Assagioli

"The soul is meant to live in and through
the body and to know itself in the heart of earthly existence."—Susan Griffin

"When the myths no longer fit
the internal plights of those who require them, the transition to
newly created myths may take the form of a chaotic voyage
to the interior; the certitude of externalization are replaced by
the anguish of the internal voyage."—Jerome Bruner

Few things bring despair like being diagnosed with cancer. Listening as the doctors talk of treating the disease aggressively reminds us that this war, like any war, is what Andrew Bard Schmookler calls "the parent and child of fears." For many, despair and fear may combine to take what is alive in our souls and transform the soul into something hard and dead. I've spoken to dozens of cancer patients about what those first few moments of learning they had cancer were like. Many of them shared that all of their attention was suddenly focused inward on themselves. They talked about withdrawing from life, viewing the world around them as a place of distrust; feeling the need to be guarded as they witnessed the awkwardness of those around them when faced with the news of their cancer.

Despair and fear, like the chemotherapy and radiation treatments, tires the body. In the words of Nietzsche, "When we are tired, we are attacked by ideas we conquered long ago." Despair can become a downward spiral as the newly diagnosed individual tries to find a way to adapt and survive. True healing of the soul doesn't seek adaptation. Instead one embraces contemplation and reflection, seeking understanding and a new perspective. In seeking the aid of helping spirits, one can restore vitality to the soul.

There is a section in T.H. White's *The Once and Future King* where Arthur, not yet having received the invitation to knighting, is despairing as he tells Merlin of his desire to become a knight and defend the world against the forces of evil. Merlyn tells Arthur that in moments of great despair, the best thing one can do is learn:

TRANSFORMING DESPAIR AND WAR WITH CANCER
THROUGH SPIRITUAL HEALING AND LEARNING

"That is the only thing that never fails. You may grow old and trembling in your anatomies, you may lie awake at night listening to the disorder in your veins, you may miss your only love, you may see the world about you devastated by evil lunatics, or know your honour trampled in the sewers of baser minds. There is only one thing then—to learn. Learn why the world wags and what wags it. That is the only thing which the mind can never exhaust, never alienate, never be tortured by, never fear or distrust, and never dream of regretting."[1]

Merlin's words remind us that no matter how challenged we are by the prospects of our illness, we each have the opportunity to turn the challenge into a time of deep learning and healing. This type of spiritual learning brings forth the healing power of wisdom, revealing possibility in the face of fear and despair.

Earlier in the book, we explored the larger terrain of the soul and how trauma-related illnesses such as cancer can be the embodiment of our internal stories waiting to be healed. Until illness strikes, we may have felt these stories were resolved. In truth, we each embody a tapestry of stories and influences that come together in search of healing.

We live in a world that wants simple answers to complex questions. When one has an illness like cancer, there is a desire to understand the how and why of our illness. We want someone to explain in simple words like, "You got this cancer because of x, y, z." So what is it about our human nature that seeks explanation and understanding as if somehow that will give us a sense of control? Spiritually we are challenged to live in the in-betweens of our understanding, the places between knowing and mystery. Such it is when we work to bring healing to cancer or any other illness we may have.

Working with the anatomy of the soul asks that we understand we are not of one mind, not of one time, not of one place, not of one illness. If cancer is an illness of how we live individually and collectively, we are each in some way connected to the healing needs of all. So their illness is ours and ours is theirs. To address illnesses like cancer only with our linear mind limits us to one way of perceiving and addressing the challenge that cancer presents. It gives us the distance and detachment we need to analyze and understand our situation, yet we also run the risk of finding ourselves in a state of numbness and denial, becoming disconnected separate. It is as Saul Bellow proclaims in *The Dean's December*, "With ordinary consciousness you can't even begin to know what's happening."

Our tendency is to analyze our predicaments through the lens of our past experiences while eliminating the possibility of new learning. We are ultimately a complex blend of many states of being all occurring at once. We are constantly moving in and out of a dream as we learn in our lives. If cancer exists in a dream we are living, we must enter the state of that dream to bring the healing that is needed.

Throughout my years of working with people with diseases of modern times (i.e. immune system diseases such as chronic fatigue, cancer, HIV, lupus, and others), I've paid close attention to the kinds of stories and themes that they're embodying. I've also observed the work done with persons diagnosed with multiple personality disorder (MPD), now known as Dissociative Identity Disorder, and included it an additional piece to the model's development. What was truly miraculous in these instances was observing a person who had severe medical conditions in one personality, and then seeing it totally disappear when another personality took over. My first witnessing of this phenomena occurred on an inpatient psychiatric unit in the 1970's.

A female patient with a diagnosed with MPD was admitted to the unit by her psychiatrist. She had been diagnosed with a colon obstruction which required removal via surgery. By history, her psychiatrist had difficulty medicating his patient due to different personalities having differing effects to the medication. Additionally, there were concerns as to what her response would be to anesthesia during surgery. During her surgery, the obstruction previously diagnosed was not present. Her psychiatrist's response at the time surmised that different personalities had different physiologies. A growing body of literature indicates the psychophysiologic differences between alter personalities in patients. Different allergic reactions, gastrointestinal and optical differences, changes in voice and handedness, effects on pain control and differences in response to medication has been documented.[1]

Dissociation is a psychological process that severs connection to a person's thoughts, feelings, memories, actions , or sense of identity. It is, in traumatic moments, an attempt to defend the soul against harm. As one patient with cancer said to me, "I chose to stay out of my body through all the chemo and radiation."

If the dissociative phenomena observed in DID suggests some aspects of extraordinary healing and creative powers, then one can also speculate that the controlled dissociation of shamanic journeying might in some ways offer the possibility of shifting the consciousness that cancer lives in.

These sorts of extraordinary and miraculous abilities have been observed in cross cultural shamanism. Sherrill Mulhern, a French anthropologist, believes that spirit possession (possession by helping spirits) observed in these traditions sheds light on the psychological phenomenon of MPD. She notes in a 1973 study that in 251 out of 488 societies reviewed, the community regularly dealt with spirit entities embodied by certain members of the group as a meaningful form of social experience. The spirits demonstrate that they are not merely from the human realm. By walking on fire, consuming toxic substances, dancing for hours without exhaustion, etc, they defy normal human limitations. An extreme example of this occurred on the island of Mayotte, where "trumba" spirits let their presence be known by ritually consuming huge amounts of food. Once these spirits left the person they had embodied, the host would often declare that they were starving. Unaware,

TRANSFORMING DESPAIR AND WAR WITH CANCER
THROUGH SPIRITUAL HEALING AND LEARNING

the trumba spirits gorged themselves while in their bodies, the individuals began eating once again. Mulhern notes that in certain cultures the spirit possession is done as a means of curing illness or distress in a person.[2]

As caveat, its important to acknowledge that there have been clients who used these methods as a form of escapism or fragmentation away from their cancer. While many cancer patients have talked about occasionally choosing to not be in their bodies in order to escape the pain or toxic effects of their treatments, they also acknowledge that this form of escape has its limits. They realize that by 'checking out' they cut themselves off from their bodies' natural abilities to heal as well cutting off their spiritual resources that can help them address their needs. Healing requires the commitment to tackle whatever presents itself as needing attention and transformation.

As a young boy, I used to attend religious services at a Jewish Nursing Home. The moments I enjoyed most were after the sharing of food when the men would gather to discuss spiritual issues. They would argue passionately, sometimes to the point of getting red in the face and looking like they were about to go toe to toe in a fight. I remember asking the rabbi, "Who is right?" His response was simply, "They are all right. Each of them has a piece of the truth." In his own way, he was saying that we all have our own journey to make and that many trails can lead to wisdom. As you participate in the following practices and exercises, remember that it is your own unique story and essence that you are working with here.

WORKING WITH CANCER'S STORY

To bring peace and healing to cancer, we must befriend and engage in relationship with it. Though we may want to avoid or to destroy that which is calling our attention, we are asked to refrain from turning cancer into the enemy. A peace approach moves us away from turning cancer into 'the Other.' Cancer itself is not evil. It is sickness seeking to be cured and made whole rather than be obliterated in the way of war.

When we are in relationship with cancer, we are joining together to learn the stories that are being expressed. It is analogous to the practice of aikido. We join our center with the center of another (in this case cancer) and we and we are curious about the intention of the attacker. We go in the direction of the attacker before bringing our attention to the aide of the helping spirits. In this way, healing direction begins with the illness. For this reason, we begin the process by journeying with the aid of helping spirits to meet the spirit of the illness.

As you review the journeys, be aware of your own personal questions. The suggestions provided are based on generalities from years of practice. One size does not fit all. As Parker Palmer in *The Courage to Teach* reminds us:

"As the process unfolds, we are reminded of a simple truth, because we cannot get inside another person's soul, we cannot possibly know the answer to another person's problem. Indeed, we cannot know exactly what the problem is."[3]

Each journey will give you information to chew on like food for your soul. Sit for awhile with the images and message you are given. Take time after each journey to slowly digest the information. It is not a race to see how quickly you can do all of the journeys. Nor is one size fits all. Listen carefully to your own inner guidance. Hopefully, you will find that there are specific questions that arise as you gain more spiritual information. Ask for clarity about what the spirits are showing you. Question the deeper meaning in what they may have said to you. Make sure to ask how to best use the information you've been given to support your healing journey. While this book offers a general perspective of suggestions that have been helpful for others, it is important to follow the integrity and wisdom of your own soul to assess your needs. In other words, follow the questions that emerge from your heart and soul.

JOURNEY EXERCISE ONE

The first journey suggestion is to once again go to your power animal and ask to be taken to meet the spirit of your illness. Some of you may not have cancer or a chronic illness that has immunological influences. Even still, remember that cancer lies as a seed in each of us. So be open to what the seed of illness has to tell you. As analogy, there was a time that it rained in a barren desert for the first time in years. Within days, a layer of beautiful little flowers emerged from the desert sands. The seeds of these flowers had been there all along, waiting for that one moment they could be express themselves. Cancer is like this in many way. If you are not currently ill, do the journey as opportunity to explore the seeds of potential illness in the terrain of your soul.

When you go to your power animal to meet the spirit of your illness, be aware that you go with your spirit helpers as a form of protection and empowerment. Some of you may be afraid to meet the spirit of your illness and what it has to share with you. As best as you can, breathe deeply and relax with the drumming. Focus on being open to what is shown to you. View it as opportunity to bring healing to whatever is waiting for you. When your helping power animal takes you to meet the spirit of the illness, be aware of everything you are being taught in that moment. Ask the spirit of the illness what its message is. Ask it, "What is your message to me?"

JOURNEY NOTES

_____

_____

_____

_____

_____

_____

_____

_____

_____

_____

_____

Take some time to reflect on what you have been given in this first journey. The experiences people have can be quite varied. Some people meet aggressive and nasty creatures which seem bent on destruction at any cost, while others meet nondescript essences which offer helpful guidance. What is most important is to honor your own experiences in your journey. Some experiences people have had are described below.

"It didn't really have much of a form, and when I asked it what it was trying to tell me, it told me that it wanted me to slow down and pay attention to what was happening in my life."

"I wasn't sure I wanted to meet the cancer and when I did it was ferocious and showed me its teeth like a wild animal. My power animal stood between us and when I asked what it was trying to tell me, it said it was angry with me and had no respect for me. I wasn't sure what I had done."

"What I met was monstrous, yet when I asked in a strong way what it was trying to tell me, it cowered before me. It said that it wanted to help me as my life was so unhealthy. I found this surprising since I'm so sick from this illness. How could it want to be helping me?"

JOURNEY EXERCISE TWO

It is an act of courage to meet one's illness, especially an illness that threatens one's life, and to begin the process of relationship. Facing our fears is an act of reclaiming our power. It moves us from experiencing our illness as something that is happening to us, to a sense that we can take action on our own behalf.

Years ago, there was a low income housing neighborhood where I was doing a lot of work with the youth at risk. The neighborhood was a mix of Southeast Asian (mostly Cambodian and Hmong), African American, and Hispanic families. I was running a group teaching some of the teenagers how to do shamanic journeying. One of the Southeast Asian boys came up to me afterwards and said, "you are doing what my uncle does." His uncle was a respected shaman in their community and the boy wanted me to meet him.

When we arrived at the building where his family lived, I noticed little creature-like figurines among the trees and bushes surrounding the building. His uncle came out to talk and expressed appreciation for my work with the young ones. After a long while of conversing, I asked him about the figurines and what they represented.

"They are the demons that play on our minds. We bring their spirits outside so they do not live in our homes. Here we feed them and provide a home for them. When visit them, they teach us and we listen."

Spiritually, this is a teaching about how to address our inner demons: our fears, worries, and anxieties. We make our illnesses the enemy and they captivate our every thought. Like every war we create, our obsessions become vigilant and relentless. Certain words invoke over and over the struggle within us. 911 is a common example of this time. Despite our best intentions, it is easy to be pulled down again and again into a negative spiral. People who have come for healing, have shared many thoughts with me. These include loss of control over their lives, disfigurement due to surgery, hair loss, feeling like a burden to others; being unable to care for themselves or lacking the life force or energy to do their work. The list goes on and on.

Shortly after meeting the Cambodian shaman, Bob came for healing help as he had been given a series of health issues with disparate diagnoses. A skilled man who worked with his hands, Bob passed out while working with power tools, but luckily avoided a serious work accident. After the incident, Bob was hospitalized, and initial medical evaluations led to a diagnoses of Multiple Sclerosis. He had shaking hands and general weakness in his legs. After a series of working hypotheses trying to explain his condition, physicians decided Bob's problems was anxiety related, and prescribed anti-anxiety medication and cognitive behavioral therapy. While some of his symptoms did decrease, he still had some problems.

While working with him, I received guidance to incorporate his "fear demon" as a part of his treatment. Bob was also certain there was something seriously wrong with his body, and I took his instincts seriously. Bob journeyed to meet the "fear demon," which in part represented the fear that he would never work again. During the journey, he met an ogre that taunted and mocked him. His power animal danced around and laughed at the ogre.

After the journey, I gave Bob instructions to make a figurine out of clay that symbolized the ogre. Then I had him journey again to capture the spirit of the ogre and blow it into the figurine he had made. His power animal instructed him where to put the figurine outside the home and told him the type of food he should offer this "fear demon." When he got home, Bob set up an altar in his flower bed and began a process of feeding and honoring the spirit. Overnight, the strength started returning to his legs and the shaking in his hands completely stopped. With the shakes gone, he was able to return to work. He also had a renewed sense of confidence in his other treatments. Bob's success with bringing peace and healing to his "fear demon" gave him the feeling that he could fight through his illness.

Now it's time for you to journey to your "demon." First, journey to your helping animal spirit with the intention of meeting the spirit of your fear/anxiety/demon. When you meet this spirit in your journey pay attention to how it looks. Ask it what it wants so you can learn more about it. When the journey ends, begin to sculpt a representation of this spirit.

Once you've finished sculpting, journey once again to meet this spirit. Go to your animal spirit to ask how you can honor this "demon." You may be given rituals or instructions on how to heal this relationship. Once you've instructions from your animal spirit, go to capture the spirit of this demon into your hands and when you return from your journey, blow the spirit of this demon into the figurine. Immediately take it outside, and create a home for it so that it is no longer living with you. Let your imagination guide you, as you create an altar space for it. If you are instructed to feed the demon, do so. It could be cookies or fruit, water or wine, or any number of things. Whatever instructions your spirit helpers give you on how to work with healing this spirit, follow them and notice what happens. If something happens to the figurine over time due to weather or animal activity, don't worry. Simply continue to work with the demon at the altar site until you know you have reached a point of healing completion.

JOURNEY NOTES

_____

_____

_____

_____

_____

_____

_____

_____

_____

_____

_____

_____

_____

_____

_____

_____

WORKING WITH THE STORY THE ILLNESS CARRIES

"Life is largely a process of adaptation to the circumstances in which we exist. A perennial give and take has been going on between living matter and its inanimate surroundings, between one living being and another, ever since the dawn of life in the prehistoric oceans. The secret of health and happiness lies in successful adjustment to the ever-changing conditions on this globe; the penalties for failure in this great process of adaptation are disease and unhappiness."—Hans Selye, *The Stress of Life*

Our souls are witnesses to all the history we have lived and that has been lived around us. By nature, our souls are adaptive and change as we need to change. It is when these adaptations, which worked as our defense against earlier traumatic challenges, get stuck in that one way of being that certain stories begin being lived out in the anatomy of the soul. When the soul is traumatized in an area of the body, the story held there is attempting to give meaning and understanding to what has been experienced. Examples of the kind of stories held in the soul were shown in the Embodied Stories chart in chapter two. These examples were derived from clinical observation of dozens of cases as well as the different types of information clients would bring back from their journeys.

These stories represent patterns of stuck-ness that block the possibility of healing and change. The blocks occur as the soul attempts to give meaning to traumatic events in our lives. The blocks in our soul become "rut stories."

These stories typically have a negative ending and repeat themselves over and over in one's life. Let's explore an example of how adaptation can become the source of emotional and spiritual paralysis.

In the story of malaria in Africa, human blood cells changed as an adaptation to protect against the disease. However, this change is also the basis for sickle cell anemia. This condition is particularly troublesome in areas with no malaria where people with this body adaptation have immigrated. Operational attack memories get infused into the cellular memory. This in turn, contributes to some cells becoming cancer (attack) cells.

Each of us carries a tapestry of stories interwoven into our beings. The challenge is to work with these stories in a multitude of ways in order to free up the places where energy is stuck and there are blockages. In part, our goal is to move our soul to a place of flowing (like a river) so there are numerous healing outlets available to us. The stories within us are not ours alone, for the soul carries not only the stories of our lives but the stories of the world around us, including the stories of our ancestors and the challenges they encountered during their lives. Our stories are as much about the details as they are about the dream. They live in every aspect of our consciousness, free from the boundaries of time—past, present, or future.

Before moving onto journeys for working with the anatomy of the soul, let's review other aspects of shamanic journeying. Journeys can involve working with helping animal spirits of the lower world, but these guides can also take us to a world in the sky, the upper world, where they work with spirit teachers in human form.

As before, close your eyes and let go of your ordinary thoughts. Take time to relax, and focus your intention on what you are seeking help for from the spiritual realm. Imagine a place that is familiar to you as your starting place. Seek a means for going up. It may be a bird that flies you on its back or carries you in their talons. You might shape shift into smoke and go up as smoke into the sky. Some of you may find climbing up a tree is your way of moving upward, while others may ride on the back of a flying horse. Once you find your method of transportation, you will go up until you hit a membrane or a layer of clouds. You will have to go through this transition to be in what is called the "upper world." Once you are here, you are seeking a teacher in human form. Each person you encounter, you must ask, "are you my teacher?" If they say "no", they may be able to direct you or take you to your teacher. Once you meet your teacher, you will ask the question that you have brought for spiritual guidance and healing.

Some of you will find that your journey to meet a teacher in the upper world is easier than when you journeyed to the lower world to find a helping animal spirit. For others of you, just the opposite will be true. In general, however, it's important that you learn how to work with the helping spirits that present themselves to you. Ultimately, you are seeking spiritual connections that work for you.

Typically, I suggest people start by journeying to learn about the story held by the spirit of the illness in the area where the cancer/illness was first discovered. If your cancer has spread and it is affecting numerous areas of the body, then journey to meet the spirit of each area separately. Working with one of your spirit helpers, journey to learn about the story embodied in each affected area of the body. Learn all you can about how it started, what it is willing to share with you, and how it is stuck or burdened by the story the illness carries.

JOURNEY NOTES

Remaining stuck in illness, and carrying its burdens, is akin to doing what one has always done and getting what you have always gotten. Simply put, healing allows for creativity and new responses rather than the habituated one. There are going to be times in our lives when we feel hopeless and lost, with no sense of direction. There is much in the psychoneuroimmunological literature that speaks about how patients with cancer who are able to express anger often have better outcomes with certain cancers than patients who feel passive and hopeless.

Since all healing in shamanism is in some way about healing relationships, you can approach the question of being blocked in other ways. You could journey to your spirit helpers and simply ask, "What caused me to get sick?" Or you could ask, "What are the spiritual relationships involved in my sickness that need balance and harmony?" As you work with different questions, you will get more and more information about how to restore balance and healing to your own life.

In every journey you take, the answers you receive may leave you with more questions that need further clarification and understanding. Assuming you have received enough clarity from the journey you just did, return with one of your spirit helpers to meet with the spirit of the illness in the area of the body that you just journeyed to. This time, ask the spirit of the illness if it would like help with unburdening and releasing the trauma it has been carrying. You may need to work with the spirit of illness for a while to gain its cooperation. Work from a place of patience, compassion, and understanding. If the illness says, "yes," then ask it whether it would like to give the burdens to fire, water, air, or earth. Once you get an answer to this question, work with the illness and your spirit helpers to facilitate the release of their burdens to the element of their choice. Each element has many forms. Water, for example, can be a drop of rain or mist or ice or a river or a lake or an ocean.

After releasing the burdens to one of the elements, ask the illness from that area of the body what it would like to fill up with now that it has released some of its burden. Ask your spirit helpers to help the spirit of the illness to fill up with those qualities it has named. It could mean standing in a beam of light and filling up, or going to a peaceful place where something healing occurs.

JOURNEY NOTES

_____

_____

_____

_____

_____

_____

_____

_____

_____

_____

_____

Two other journeys you may wish to consider here are:

1. Journey to learn how to heal a memory in your cells that no longer serves you. Perhaps it once served to help protect you, but is no longer working in the ways originally intended.

2. Journey for a new story that guides you in a new way of living your life and helps support your healing.

A DIFFERENT SENSE OF TIME

"For everything there is a season, and a time for every purpose under heaven: A time to be born, and a time to die; a time to plant, and a time to pluck up that which is planted; a time to kill, and a time to heal; a time to break down and a time to build up; a time to weep, and a time to laugh; a time to mourn and a time to dance; a time to cast away stones, and a time to gather stones together; a time to embrace and a time to refrain from embracing; a time to seek and a time to lose; a time to keep and a time to cast away; a time to rend and a time to sew; a time to keep silence and a time to speak; a time to love and a time to hate; a time for war and a time for peace." Ecclesiastes It is said that when shamans journey, they journey outside of time and space. The soul is able to journey beyond the place of beginning. Past, present, and future are all the same in spiritual time. In simple ways, you may have already noted that when you've journeyed a few minutes it seems much longer. You may come back with so much information that you perceive being gone for a long time. This kind of time distortion is often described when one goes into deep states of trance.

Time is like a river. When we step into the river of time, we become like the water that ebbs and flows, changing from moment to moment. Time, like the river, is a shifting pattern of realities; realities that are always in a state of flux. Time in this realm is very different than in the spiritual realm.

Time, in essence, is relative. In any given moment, some parts of us may be ill and out of balance while others remain quite healthy. The seeds of cancer and other chronic illnesses are not bound by time. Traumas of long ago may come to haunt us years later as they often do for persons with PTSD. Cancer has its own way of taking us back through time and into our future at the same time.

Consider the example of the person with a multi-personality disorder who has an illness in one personality at one time, while the other personality at another time has no illness.

Spiritual illness and health exist outside the construct of time. Experience this for yourself as you journey to your helping spirits and ask them to take you to a time before the conditions for cancer were in your body. Learn as much as you can about that time of balance, harmony and health. The intent here is to reconnect the soul to this time and bring the body towards its own healing possibility. It does not matter whether you do this as an upper or lower world journey. Follow your instincts as to what seems right for you.

JOURNEY NOTES

_____

_____

_____

_____

_____

_____

_____

_____

_____

_____

_____

There are certain journeys that lend themselves to being done with the healing support of your friends, family, and community. Occasionally it has been useful to wrap the person with cancer, the person doing the journey, in a white sheet and then gently lay them in a soft hole in the earth. Ritualizing this journey or other journeys like it helps the person with cancer feel the loving support that is there for them, both in terms of their community as well as in the spirit realm.

The following is a story of a journey-within-ritual that was shared with me: A woman with breast cancer asked a group of her friends to wrap her in a white sheet and carry her to a place on her land where she wanted to do the journey. Her friends decided to sing the song "Return Again" as they carried her. "Return again, return again, return to the home of your soul. Return to who you are, return to what you are, return to where you are, born and reborn again...." They then lowered her into a spot of soft pine needles amongst her favorite pines.

The woman reports. "It scared me because I kept going back and back in time through my life with the help of my teacher until I was maybe two years old. I started to feel bad that I had been out of balance for so long, when my teacher reminded me that I had had a lot of wonderful moments in my life and asked me to name moments that felt very blessed to me. I found that came easily. When we returned to the two year old, I remembered that one of my grandparents had died then. I think it was my mother's father, and realized that she may have been very sad. At the same time, I was aware of how loved I felt as I was being carried to this place. I knew I was not alone and a feeling of deep peace filled me. I knew then I would be OK."

ANCESTORS NOT GENETICS

Except for a limited number of cancers, evidence of a genetic link to the development of cancer is rare. Nonetheless, many people who come for help, share stories of other family members who have had cancer. In certain shamanic traditions, a repetitive pattern of struggle with health or other issues

TRANSFORMING DESPAIR AND WAR WITH CANCER
THROUGH SPIRITUAL HEALING AND LEARNING

within a family is considered to be an ancestral-related illness. Phrases like the, "sins of the ancestors may visit upon the decendants" allude to a notion that the troubles of an earlier generation may effect the one's yet to come.

Ancestral soul work speaks to the notion that the traumas of the past may create problems for later descendants. Much of this may be in the patterns of how families deal with trauma, loss, and stress. Many people living in the U.S. had ancestors that came to this country in order to escape something and to find a better dream. Consider how much you know about your ancestors? Do you know stories of what they went through? Did they not want to talk about the old country? How did they deal with stress and trauma? How much did their patterns of survival get passed down? Lifestyle choices that are unhealthy, such as eating patterns, patterns of denying emotions, and patterns of unhealed family issues are what we are talking about here. The following story demonstrates this point:

A man of Irish Catholic descent came from a family history where all the men died in their early 40's. He was determined to not fall into the family story. He kept fit, did not drink alcohol, and was a devout Catholic. Yet there he was fighting an aggressive form of prostate cancer that had not responded to surgery, chemotherapy, and radiation. On the one hand, he knew he was dying, but on the other he was angry and determined that he would not be another man in the family leaving the earth before his time. Talking of his family history, he knew that they had left after the potato famine and a little after the civil war in the U.S. There were murmurs of something bad having happened with a great-great grandparent, but he did not know what.

At that point, we discussed having him journey on the question, "What is the healing that the ancestors are asking of me?" It led to more discussion about what had happened to different family members along the way, including other cancer situations. At that point, he made a comment, "My being sick is a lot bigger than me, isn't it?"

This is how he described his journey: "I met a teacher in the upper world that was new to me. He looked like he could have been an ancestor of mine. He takes me to the village where my ancestors dwelled and I watched a fight over money and a woman. The teacher tells me to keep watching. As the two men fight, one thrashes the other until he can't get up. As he is walking away, the man on the ground says, "You and your family will live in hell." My teacher tells me to comfort this man. We go to the him and I wash off his face and hands. I offer him a towel and help him get up. He asks me who I am and I tell him I'm from the future, and that I think one of my family members just beat the hell out of him. I tell him I'm sorry and offer to buy him a drink since we are outside a place that seems like a pub. My teacher nods at me as if to say "good." The man puts his arm over my shoulder and I watch us go into the pub.

After the journey, he reported feeling like something had shifted in his body. He talked of how he had tried to not have a temper his whole life or be a fighter because of he saw other family members as hot-headed. He realized that he would need to fight if he were going to survive his own cancer. A week later he called to report that his PSA had dropped considerably. He lived four quality years beyond what his diagnostic picture had presented.

If it feels right for you and your situation, journey to the upper world to ask your spirit teacher the following question: "What is the healing that the ancestors are asking of me?"

JOURNEY NOTES

_____

_____

_____

_____

_____

_____

_____

_____

_____

_____

_____

_____

TRANSFORMING DESPAIR AND WAR WITH CANCER
THROUGH SPIRITUAL HEALING AND LEARNING

HEART AS OUR BEST PATH

In some cancers, the cancers create energetic barriers around themselves that block medicines from getting through. While people in imagery work to minimize the side effects of chemotherapy, this raises a larger question of, "how can I get through the barriers of the cancer to bring healing to the illness?" In certain cases that would be a good question to journey on.

In spiritual terms, our hearts are the seats of the immune system. When we bring heart to our healing journey, we are activating the natural healing ability of our bodies. Some of us may feel disheartened by the predicament we find ourselves in, believing it to be proof that we lost heart long ago. We may yearn for what brings heart to our lives yet block its possibility through old patterns of defense. A journey that can help you work through this is: Journey to your spirit helpers and ask them what you defend against seeing, hearing, feeling and getting to your hearts. Listen closely to their guidance.

JOURNEY NOTES

_____

_____

_____

_____

_____

_____

_____

TRANSFORMING DESPAIR AND WAR WITH CANCER
THROUGH SPIRITUAL HEALING AND LEARNING

Gratitude is ultimately the spiritual anecdote for blockage. Brother David Steindl-Rast contends that, "Gratefulness is the gentle power that restores courage." So often, I will hear people talk about trips they took to work with indigenous shamans around the world. More often than not, they talk about the happiness and gratitude they witnessed among the indigenous people, even though they had very little materially. The practice of gratitude builds resiliency, which enhances our capacity to embrace challenge and change. It's also been shown to reduce signs of stress, and to help us respond more creatively to our own healing needs.

A spiritual practice created by Dr. Martin Seligman and discussed on his *Reflective Happiness* website, is a simple practice for working with developing a sense of gratitude. Each evening, bring to mind three blessings you are grateful for. Then note your part in making each blessing happen. It serves as a reminder that we always have choices and there are things we can do. It may be as simple as taking the time to watch a sunset or smiling at a young child, or noticing how good it felt to take a deep breath. Most importantly, note blessings that feel authentic to you. When we pretend gratitude, our souls go crooked. The effect is a loss of energy and passion for what we are doing. After making it part of your daily practice for a couple of weeks, take a moment to notice how you've been feeling over that period of time.

Sharing our gratitude, and our stories are important aspects of healing. When I was a young boy dreaming with my great aunt Soshie, she always asked me about what was troubling my soul and about the dreams I had been having. Then she would have a special dream for me, and she would say what I say to you now.

"We must now have a piece of honeycake, so we can remember what is sweet in our lives today."

Just as Merlin said about learning in times of despair, "it never fails."

CHAPTER 5

Cancer and Place

"The trees are dying. The plants are
dying. This place is dying. No one sings for the trees anymore. No one
sings for the plants anymore. No one sings for this place anymore. You must
remember to sing"—Corbin Harney, SHOSHONE MEDICINE MAN,
as told to author while on a sacred walk

"Our ancestors told us that
land is sacred, that animals and plants are our relatives, and that it
is our duty to ensure that they are defended for the next generation."
—Victoria Tauli-Corpus, *Igorot people of the Philippines*

It may seem unusual to consider our relationship to "place" in our journey
to make peace with cancer. Beyond knowing that environmental exposures
could play a contributing role in the development of disease, most of us don't
think of place as having a part in the overall healing process. Nor do we
think that separation from our ancestors' homelands hurts our souls.

At the same time, if I asked the question, "Are there places you've been that you've felt a special connection to?" Many of you could immediately recall images of those places as well as the positive feelings associated with them. Conversely, you may also recall places you've been where the 'vibes' felt bad or where bad things occurred in your past are still very much with you in memory.

Many indigenous people have a different way of thinking about place. They believe that places have healing energies, and that these energies will speak to us if we take the time to listen. It is from this viewpoint that we'll explore how the spiritual history of places can affect us. We will also explore methods you can use for your own healing.

A DIFFERENT VIEW OF PLACE

In a world of six billion people it is estimated that two billion are displaced. People from all around the world have migrated, seeking safety from both natural disasters and war. Recent migrations include the Iraqis people and the people of Sudan leaving war-torn regions and the former residents of New Orleans that were displaced by Hurricane Katrina.

We are living in a time of migration, in which the traumas of the relatively recent past are keeping us locked in the present. Meanwhile, we seemed to have forgotten our collective history. Even so, the stories of the past dwell in our bodies and in the places we now dwell. The history of these places and the things that need to be healed have been imported in the great migration of humanity. Each place has become a melting pot of our earthly history, with cancer and other illnesses calling upon us to heal the story of our lives on this earth.

There is a word among the Ojibway, "nishnabe," which means "the land to which the people belong." Tribal knowing says we do not own the land, it owns us. We are spiritual people influencing and being influenced by all that is around us. Each place has its own influence, its own vibration, and when both our ancestors and we were pulled from our home, we brought some of that place with us, just as we left something of ourselves behind. It is the land that gives us our identity and our sense of who we are. Some of us may feel the pull of our ancestral homeland calling us to know who we are. While we may remember what was left behind through story, more often than not, we have become disconnected from the story of our ancestral displacement. The shame or pain of what was left behind went untold, as if forgetting would make the pain go away. I have learned that this is not so.

When I was a child, my great aunt Soshie showed me a little bag of dirt. It was soil she had brought with her from Russia. She took my hands placed them on the soil and said, "This is who you are. This is where you are from." She believed that in our separation from place we had become an a-historical people, and that it was causing a sickness in our souls. Its symptoms were being stuck in the present, an inability to learn from the lessons of the past, and not being able to connect how we live now to the future generations. Aunt Soshie taught me that place communicates to us in rhythm and vibration and gives context to our larger world. When we forget "our place" we lose our capacity for compassion and our understanding of how we affect the world around us. Unless we relearn the spiritual meaning of place, all forms of life could face displacement and illness.

For indigenous people the relationship to place defines an entire cultural identity. This is clear when we hear the words of one Cherokee who, while protesting the building of a dam in the Tennessee Valley said, "If we were to make our offerings at a new place, the spiritual beings would not know us. We would not know the mountains or the significance of them. We would not know the land and the land would not know us. We would not know the sacred places. If we were to go on top of an unfamiliar mountain we would not know the life forms that dwell there."[1]

Restoring our sacred relationship to the lands in which we belong is a story of our world. For those of us who were displaced by war or poverty, famine or environmental pollution so long ago we have forgotten, now is the time to remember. For it is through story that truth comes forth in the soul. When we are displaced, we lose our sense of inner harmony. When we do not know the place we are at, we are truly lost. Because cancer sets our world on edge, it has the capacity to leave us feeling lost.

RESTORING RIGHT RELATIONSHIP TO PLACE: A Teaching Story

At an international conference, I met a South African attorney who had been involved in the anti-apartheid movement. At the end of apartheid, he became a land-rights attorney representing tribal people that had been displaced from their sacred land due to the apartheid. In one particular instance he was asked to represent the San people (Bushmen) and help them regain their land.

This was during the early days of the Mandela administration so there was little desire to deal with tribal land rights cases. Instead, the focus was on creating stability, and a process of healing and reconciliation. Nonetheless, this lawyer spent several years on the case. He described the land the Elders wanted returned as a place devoid of life. Once lush with water and vegetation and animals, it was now totally dry and desolate following years of drought.

As a white South African, this attorney could not understand the desire of the Elders to return to a land he viewed as dead. The Elders said to him, "When we get our land back it will rain. The animals will return, the plants will return and we the people will return." Although it seemed crazy from his point of view, the attorney continued working on this case and others like it. After a couple of years, it became clear that the courts were going to rule in favor of restoring the land rights to the tribe. Excited by the news, he got into his personal plane and flew up to tell the Elders.

Upon his arrival, he told the Elders that the courts were moving toward resolution of the case and that the land was going to be returned to their people. As he was telling them the news, one cloud in the sky hovered over the gathering and it began to rain on him and him alone. He remembered the Elders saying, "When the lands are returned it will rain." He began to cry, which he found startling, and said, "You were right, it is raining." The Elders shook their heads, "No," they said. "When we return to the land it will rain."

Three months later the courts ordered the land returned to the people. On that day and for the next six weeks, it rained. Years of drought ended miraculously. The grasses grew. The water holes filled up. The animals came back. And once again, the people returned to the land where they belonged.

HISTORY AND PLACES

"Some things you never forget… Places, places are still there. If a house burns, it's gone, but… the picture of it… stays, and not just in my memory, but out there in the world. What I remember is a picture floating around out there outside my head. I mean, even if I don't think it, even if I die, the picture of what I did, or knew or saw is still there. Right in the place where it happened… Where I was before I came here, that place is real. It's never going away." From *Beloved* by Toni Morrison.

Many years ago, I heard Carolyn Myss speaking at a bookstore. She told a story of a village near the Ukraine/Belarus border where the Nazis had gathered up all the Jews in the area and herded them into the local synagogue. Once the building was filled, they set it on fire. All the people perished. The name of this place is Chernobyl. The very spot the synagogue had burned down was the very spot that reactor number 4 at the Chernobyl complex melted down.

When the radiation cloud developed over the broken reactor, the winds shifted in an unusual direction, causing the radiation cloud to head directly towards Germany and later towards Sweden. When German scientists noticed rising radiation levels they alerted German public television to warn people, particularly pregnant women and young children to stay inside. A few hours later, the German government censured this announcement and told people there was nothing to worry about. As a result, increased rates in cancers, particularly thyroid cancer, have been noted by survivors of the immediate area of the disaster, but also as far as away as Sweden.

The death toll from the Chernobyl disaster has always been misrepresented. According to the Ukrainian government, there were 6,400 casualties related to the Chernobyl explosion over 20 years. Translated this means elevated cancers and leukemia. More perplexing yet is that we just don't know how long this will last or how dangerous it really is. Once released, radiation is very hard to manage. While nature is surviving in the areas surrounding Chernobyl, they still remain largely uninhabitable by humans due to high radiation levels.

Currently, about five million people live in areas of Belarus, the Russian Federation, and Ukraine where the levels of radioactive caesium deposition are more than 37 kBq/m2. About a quarter of a million people continue to live in areas classified as strictly controlled zones where contamination exceeds 555 kBq/m2. The World Health Organization conducted a series of reviews between 2003 and 2005. A large increase in the incidence of thyroid cancer had occurred among people who were young children and adolescents at the time of the accident and who lived in the most contaminated areas. Radioactive iodine was deposited in pastures eaten by cows and was then concentrated it in their milk, which was subsequently drunk by children. A case study of such an incident follows:

After hearing a presentation in St. Petersburg, Russia, Natasha came to me for shamanic healing. She was a graduate student in her early twenties with a large thyroid tumor the size of a grapefruit extending from her throat area. Outwardly, she was emotionally flat as she talked about her cancer and the impending surgery. She shared her fear of being in a relationship or getting married because her babies might be born deformed. (Certainly a number of birth deformities had been noted as a result of the radiation exposure.) In my journey to the spirits, I was guided to return lost soul parts from age 3 and 5. Both ages were filled with images of her father's drunkenness and anger. I was directed to sing a song to the tumor: a song of lamentation and sorrow. The melody was dramatic and painful. Eventually, I started singing the tumor's response to the song. By the end of the healing session, the tumor had shrunk to half its size. A year later, the young woman came to see me again. Her cancer had been successfully treated, she was engaged to be married, and her presence was much brighter.

This type of sorrow and flatness were common to the several Chernobyl thyroid cancer cases I worked on. One wonders what it is that causes some of the young people to later develop thyroid cancer but not others. I have met dozens of people who lived near Chernobyl in their earlier years, and the most striking difference among them is the sorrow and flatness seen in the ones with cancer. The same can be said of the Shoshone Nation who live near nuclear test sites, or the people that live near toxic and polluted sites or in any number of smog-filled areas throughout the world.

HISTORY OF PLACES AS CANCER

My great aunt Soshie believed that a place's negative history presented itself in the form of elemental imbalances. For her, Chernobyl was a place of fire that was too hot for more fire. The element of fire, analogous to cancer, must be fed to stay alive and so it feeds on everything it possibly can to maintain itself. We often forget that we are spiritual beings subject to influences from the spiritual fields around us. These spiritual fields call to us for healing so sickness will not prevail. A specific place may evoke imbalances that are within us that are calling out for healing. It is equally true that what needs healing in the place itself must also be healed if those who live there are to be in balance and harmony. When we heal the history that has been created by humans, we heal the place and in doing so restore the power that is inherent in that place. When we heal the past, we bring forth healing to the present and to those times yet to come.

The story of Chernobyl is not simply a story of a nuclear disaster. It reflects a history of war on the earth. The twentieth century was the most devastating time in our collective human history. This is true in terms of loss of life and the extreme devastation to the earth. When war is declared on a people the modern weapons also declare war on the earth. The soil, the water, the air and the people living in those places are affected in far-reaching ways.

A report from the United Nations Environment Program in 2004 estimated that four million pounds of low-level radioactive dust; residue from depleted uranium now covers a good portion of Iraq. Depleted uranium has a half-life of 4.7 billion years 2, so we can only speculate about what that exposure will ultimately mean for soldiers and civilians alike. We could just as easily substitute Agent Orange, which has been linked to contributive causation of Non-Hodgkin's lymphoma in Vietnam vets. Yet most of us still do not know what the lasting effects are in Vietnam.

We know war kills and that, "war begets war." While many of us may think of a specific war as something that happened in the past, in truth, its effects may linger for generations. Like people, places can have soul loss. The trauma of war brings a loss-of-life force to a place. That loss of vitality can remain in a place for a very long time. We are reminded of words ascribed to Chief Seattle: "What we do to the earth, we do to ourselves." Places remember the violence and sickness brought to them. While they don't necessarily become places of violence, they do hold the pain of what has happened there.

WORKING WITH PLACE FOR HEALING

There are a lot of stories of shamans and spiritual people such as Buddha and the Baal Shem Tov, who sat in nature and received messages and wisdom that later became part of their teachings. Places also become known for their healing powers. Some places are quite renowned, like the healing waters of Lourdes, France. Perhaps there are places you've been where afterwards you noticed feeling much better. As a personal example, I had a severe foot injury that would not heal and made walking painful. While on a vacation on the island of Kauai and without really thinking about It, I noticed one day that my foot was no longer hurting. Later I was told that Kauai was known as the island of healing. Shamans were known to do healing work at the places they believed supported healing of the people.

That being said, it is not an invitation to go on pilgrimage seeking such a place. They exist everywhere. Many have simply been lost or forgotten in the migration of people. Others are kept alive through story. As an example, Cheyenne legends speak of a place in the Midwest United States that has been a sacred place of healing. In the legend, it is said that a buffalo would rise up from the earth and show itself to the people again. A very small story in the newspaper managed to find its way to a Cheyenne medicine man. This story spoke of a farm field where a big rock had emerged from the earth. The rock was described as looking like the head of a buffalo. The news excited him so he called his sons that same morning. He asked them to immediately drive him several hundred miles to this site. Arriving in the early evening, the farmer welcomed the medicine man and took him to the place in his fields where the buffalo rock had risen. Through his prayers and spiritual work, the medicine man was certain that the place of healing known to his people had returned as prophesied.

In many indigenous traditions, places are dreaming to us. Each place has its own story and gifts. The film, *Where the Green Ants Dream* illustrates this beautifully. The indigenous people of Australia are upset by the uranium mining being conducted by the British because the noise will keep the brilliantly green colored ants from dreaming the future. Meanwhile, the supervisor for the mining company comes to the realization that the tons of holes his company has drilled into the earth are destroying the environment and that the material they've gathered in the drilling process can also destroy the world. In the movie, there is a wonderful scene where indigenous men are in the shoe polish aisle of a big grocery store right at the place where "the tree of children" had stood before it was chopped down in the building of the store. This tree was where they would gather to dream their children into existence. Unsuccessful in keeping the men out, the store owner moved items not normally shopped for to that aisle. Unfazed, the men continued to sit in a circle, playing their didgeridoos, chanting, and dreaming their future babies. The film offers an indigenous view of the power and possibility of place. It also reminds us of the environmental damage of uranium mining and of uranium to our health.

Places also talk to us through resonance. Our soul communicates to our body this way, too. See for yourself. Go out into nature holding the intention to find a place that has healing power for you. Notice where you are being pulled. It may be a park or a tree in your yard or a local body of water. Nature is everywhere, including the city, and any of these places can call you as much as a trip to the countryside

When you find a place that draws you to it, sit there for a while. Notice what is happening around you as you. Messages are there in the circumference that surrounds you. Here's a story to help illustrate the point:

A young man is distraught and depressed and goes out to a local lake to get away. For some reason, he is drawn to crawl on his belly through a briar patch to get to the lakeshore. Once through he sits down, wanting to be alone. In that place he discovered that in nature, we are never alone. Hundreds of monarch and swallowtail butterflies were nesting in the area, and many came and landed on him. He began to notice their gentleness and how slowly they opened and closed their wings. He noticed their fragility and their strength. As the winds blew the butterflies simply floated in place, seemingly effortlessly. He noticed how bright the sun shone on the place and how it seemed to be part of what drew the butterflies there. There were wild-flowers all along the banks, yet the butterflies were landing on him. His own breathing and rhythm slowed to the rhythm of the wings and he noticed how relaxed he was becoming. In his mind, he thought the butterflies were teaching him how to meditate. As he continued to focus on being with the butterflies, he realized that the things that had been troubling him suddenly did not seem so great, and solutions began to pop into his mind.

I suggest that you take time to go to a place in nature with a question in your heart and mind; something you are seeking help with. Make sure the question is of great importance to you so that your intention is strong. As you wander among this place, notice where you feel compelled to go. It will feel like a magnet is pulling you there. Once there, pay attention to everything that occurs. In the space below, make notes for yourself about the things that catch your attention. It could be a strong event or a subtle movement that speaks to you. Write it all down. Then after a 30 minutes or so, look at what you have written. Sit and think about how the things shown to you could be answers to your question.

JOURNEY NOTES

_____

_____

_____

_____

_____

_____

_____

_____

_____

_____

_____

_____

_____

When we are given spiritual information, it must be worked with to make sure we are clear in our understandings. Take what you have learned thus far and do one or two journeys for more information. Suggestions for the journeys are: What is drawing me to this place for my healing? How are the messages I've received from this place providing answers to my question? How can I use this place to help me with my healing?

Perhaps there is a place you have visited in your life that had a healing effect for you. Journey to that place to reconnect with the powers that are there and ask, "What is it about this place that is healing for me?"

_____

_____

_____

_____

_____

_____

_____

_____

_____

_____

_____

_____

_____

When we visit a place in nature, there are many inhabitants there. In the place you sat, there are numerous patterns in interconnection. There may be trees and lots of plants, insects and animals, wind, sun and moon, clouds, water and stones. In the world of the shamans all of these have a spirit and are alive. Each one is a part of the balance of life, and each one has powers that can be used for healing. In many shamanic cultures, the shamans will spiritually connect with plants to learn which plant could be used as medicine for the spiritual illness a person has. The CDC website notes that 70 percent of the plants used in medicine for cancer treatment comes from rainforests that are currently under ecological threat. In the ways I was taught, each plant has a resonance that brings healing to the discordant resonance of an illness. Another way to say this is that the plant sings the healing. While you were at your place you may have found yourself drawn to a particular plant. Maybe in some way it was speaking to you. If you wish, you can go out into nature and ask for a plant that wants to work with you in healing a sickness you carry. Simply notice what you have been drawn to and then journey to meet the spirit of that plant. Then ask it how to work with it for your healing. It may or may not involve taking it orally as spiritual medicine.

JOURNEY NOTES

_____

_____

_____

_____

_____

_____

_____

_____

_____

_____

_____

_____

_____

_____

Places can also make us sick. A place, like Love Canal on the eastern side of Niagara Falls, is an obvious example. A former chemical dumpsite, it was covered over with dirt and later sold to the city for a dollar. A community was built on the site only to have chemical explosions other toxic disasters occur. Epidemiological data showed much higher rates of birth defects in this area as well as high rates of leukemia. While the shattered dreams and sicknesses of Love Canal are well-known stories, the spiritual questions are different. The Love Canal disaster is often cited as an example of people being traumatized by an environmental event that caused extreme pain and suffering.

William Love was the original owner of the tract of land that was later named after him. His original dream was to build a canal connecting to Niagara Falls, and to utilize the water flow to power an electric plant for the area. As the dream failed, what was left was an unfinished ditch. The site was then sold and became used as a toxic dumpsite. Spiritually, we are called to ask, "Why here?" The first step in learning how to bring healing to a place that has become sick is to journey to the guardian spirit of that place. Go with your spirit helpers to learn about what has happened here, and more importantly, ask them how can you help heal the place. Prior to doing this journey, review the following cases to help clarify things in your mind.

A number of people that lived in a high-rise condo started noticing that several of their neighbors had gotten quite ill. Afraid there was something wrong with the building they called in inspectors. After checking for possible sick-building clues like mold, they find nothing. One person in the group came to me and asked for spiritual help. After meeting up with my power animal, I journeyed to the guardian spirit of the place. The spirit presented itself as an old Native American. He told me the place was originally a burial site for his people and he was angry because it had been desecrated. When I asked how the issue could be healed, it became clear that his main concern was honoring the dead. After leaving the place spirit, the power animal suggested a yearly ritual to honor the dead who were buried on this land. I shared this information with the woman who had come to me for help. She confirmed that there were indeed sacred mounds in the area. Knowing there could also have been burial mounds at the site of the condo, she organized people to do the prescribed ritual. Coincidence or not, she reported that things had improved; not only had people's health improved, but there were also no new cases.

In the second case, a man had returned from a foreign country where he'd been a missionary. A relatively young man, he'd had one major health issue after another. Each one was getting progressively worse and he had been recently diagnosed with colon cancer. He personally felt he was made sick by the place itself. Given his strong feelings about this, I accepted it as so and did a healing journey on his behalf. The place spirit I encountered was angry with the earlier colonizers who had come and disrupted traditional practices of honoring the place spirits. They had cut down trees and built buildings without any regard for the place itself. Advocating on the man's behalf, I pointed out that he had come to help and wanted to help restore old traditions. This spiritual intervention seemed to calm the place spirit. Healing work was then done with the man. Afterwards, he reported feeling that a huge weight had been lifted. He listened to the journey story with great interest and said he did want to help restore old traditions there. A few weeks later he called to report that his health was better and that he had started a project to raise money to support the traditional healers of the area.

Visiting the spirit of place speaks to those situations where there seems to be a pattern of cases that are related a spot, as cited in the studies above. In rare instances, there could be a situation where someone visited a place and that place made them feel sick. If that were to you, you should go with one of your spirit helpers to meet the guardian spirit of that place. Tell the spirit why you are there. Ask what it wants to tell you and what it needs from you.

JOURNEY NOTES

_____

_____

_____

_____

_____

WORKING WITH OURSELVES

Facing a chronic, potentially life-threatening illness like cancer, leads us to do a lot of introspection about regrets or unfinished business. Often those moments are associated with places in our lives. For example:

I had a patient who, due to illness, was at a critical juncture in his life. He told me about growing up with an explosive, alcoholic father and a mother who was quite depressed and needy and how he had to bury his emotions. He attended Catholic school, and when he tried to get help there for his situation at home. Instead of receiving support he felt the message he received was to, "shut up and honor your parents no matter what."

As an adult, he had left the church. He described his life as spiritually bereft, his existence lonely. He felt there was something missing in his life. As he faced the prospect that he might be dying, he realized how tired he was of the emptiness. As I listened, his words described soul loss, yet I also sensed a longing for something that was once in this man's childhood. It was the sense of identity he'd had as a Catholic.

His own journey showed him that he had abandoned himself in the old Catholic School he had attended. After going for help there and being let down, he literally got stuck in this place. His journey also spoke to him about going back to the school and walking through his history there. He needed to feel all the feelings that would come up and give voice to them. Most importantly, he was to reclaim himself there. And so he went back.

He described walking in his old neighborhood, feeling himself coming back to life. A young priest allowed him to walk in the schoolrooms. He was comfortable with the priest and told him why he was doing this. The priest was supportive, and told him he was sorry that he wasn't heard at a time he really needed to be heard. The man asked the priest if he would be willing to counsel him on how to find peace with the church, and the priest agreed to do so. Later, the patient reported that regardless of what happened with his health, walking through the school had been a profoundly uplifting ritual for him. He expressed gratitude to the spirits and felt a strong sense that he had returned home. While he was quite ill, his chemotherapy and radiation went easier than expected. With his treatment, he went into remission.

Places remember you as you remember them. Take time to think about places in your life and times in your own history which feel unsettled in some way. Journey to see if there is history in places that are calling to you for a healing resolution of some sort. Ask your spirit helpers for guidance on how to bring healing to these issues.

JOURNEY NOTES

ALL PLACES ARE SACRED

There is a Native American saying, "Heal Seven Generations Backward and Seven Generations Forward." Often when I work with traumatized populations, such as youth at risk or prison inmates, I ask them how much they know about their ancestors. Almost always the answer is, "little to nothing." Many of them don't even know where their families are from. Some share that their grandparents never wanted to talk about the past. I, in turn, tell them that what happened there was brought here and left there at the same time. In other words, the pain came here while the land there remembers what happened.

As I work with these populations and help them to heal backward, our aim is to bring healing to the lessons of history so it doesn't feed our present. As we dream forward to future generations, these individuals are freed from the baggage of past generations, which frees them up to live a better life in the here and now.

As part of healing backwards, we give thanks to the ancestors for all they did to help us be here and for all the wisdom they have to share. The ancestors know the challenge of life and have much wisdom to share. As we heal forward we take the lessons of the past and pause, giving deep thought to the actions we take now.

Through the years, a number of my patients have felt strongly that what gave their lives meaning and direction after receiving a cancer diagnosis was living life more purposively, and giving back whenever they could.

A number of clients I've worked with have found that place has played an important part in creating healing in their souls. Because of this, many of them have felt compelled to work on healing the past, and the land of their ancestors. Others have felt drawn to work on cleaning up the poisons in the environment that contribute to disease. Doing work around place has reminded each of them that they belong here and that it is important to take care of the places they call home.

Finding a way to restore purpose and meaning has been an important part of the healing process to a number of patients I've worked with over the years. It has been especially vital for people who are working on issues of place and who want to heal the wounds of the ancestors. For this reason, I suggest that you consider doing a journey to the upper world to ask your teacher, "How can I give purpose and meaning to my life?"

CHAPTER 6

Death, Dreaming, and Remembering

"Help me to know the shortness
of life so that I may gain wisdom of the heart."—Psalm 90

"Raven wanted to create people. He
fashioned humanlike shapes out of stone. He blew his breath into the stones
and they came alive. But soon they were dead again. Then he made humanlike
shapes out of earth. And blew his breath into them and they came alive. But
soon they were dead again. He carved humans out of wood and blew his breath
onto them and once again they came alive. And soon they were dead again.
Then he made humans out of the grass and blew his breath onto them.
They came alive and were the ancestors of the human race. From then on
people grew up and died back like grass."—Tlingit parable, ALASKA

In many ways we are always preparing for death. A friend or family member
dies. Our job is terminated because of cutbacks. Something we once believed is

no longer true and the belief is shattered. It is said that every shamanic journey one takes is a mini death; a practice for our soul's departure upon death.

The diagnosis of cancer almost always brings up the issue of death. Upon hearing the word cancer, questions abound. "Am I going to die? How long do I have to live? What are my chances of staying alive? Will I suffer? What will happen to me physically, emotionally and spiritually? What will happen to my loved ones?" To paraphrase the words of a Lakota Elder during a walk together, "Death is everywhere. No one escapes death, so why fear it? I know I can't avoid it."

As a young boy, I often went to the Jewish nursing home before going to Hebrew school. I visited the old people and listen to their stories. I knew my visits brightened their day. I also knew that my soul needed to drink in their stories of the old country, the old ways, and the wisdom they had gained along the way. There was always the risk that the next time I visited someone I had befriended would not be there. The times I went to a room and saw the bed stripped bare, I was left feeling sad and empty. In this place, death was a constant. Yet their stories became a salve for my soul, and these memories made me stronger.

There were times during my visits with my great aunt Soshie that I talked about stories I had heard at the nursing home. Stories about how hard life was back in Russia or Poland or Belorussia or the Ukraine. She had lived many of these stories, so what interested her most was my response to them. "What did you learn from the stories?" she'd ask. "What did they teach you about life, and more importantly, living?" For her, spiritual lessons lived in every observation and story told. If I talked about being sad over a particular person's death, she'd ask me what I had learned from them. I'd tell her and she would point to my heart and say, "they live here." Or if I sensed that someone who had died was still around, she might say, "Maybe they needed to tell you one more story?" Then I'd tell her the story I most remembered from that person. In response, she would often say, "It is a good thing to re-member." Always she would dream a dream for me at the end of these talks. Once I asked her, "What would happen if we stopped dreaming?" Her answer was short and succinct, "We die." After a short pause, she grabbed my little hand. "But we dream to live. Let me get you some honey cake and together, we'll remember the sweetness of life."

Aunt Soshie believed that the spiritual lessons one gained through illness were an important part of a healing journey and for that reason one should not hold back their thoughts and reactions to that illness.

FINDING OUR SOULS IN THE FACE OF DEATH

The ordinary mind is reactionary. It is busy analyzing and judging. Its focus is on survival and personality. Personality is clothing we create in our fear, de-nial, and grief. In those times of reaction, the ordinary mind is locked in the present moment. It is in some ways akin to the deer frozen in the face of the headlights. Facing death does not necessarily induce dying. It is the means through which we let go of attachments and find our essence. A central tenet of most spiritual traditions is that pain and suffering, loss and sorrow, carry within them the keys that unlock the gates of spiritual experience.

Just as it is natural to think about death when given a diagnosis of cancer, it is natural to be afraid. It is ironic that we talk about going to war with cancer, but think of peace with death. I've noticed that when I read obituaries I often find a common description of the deceased. For example, "After fighting a long and courageous battle with cancer, they have at last come to a place of peace." In my experience of working with people diagnosed with cancer, real peace came for them as they embraced the needs they had in the face of death. There are four basic needs I have witnessed occurring over and over again in the healing journey with patients. They are:

1. A need to find the meaning in their lives. To know that in some way they learned something, that they made a difference in another's life, that they shared themselves in a significant way, and that they gave/received love.

2. A need to heal their relationships with close family members and friends. To use the time to make a connection and to be able to let go of issues they had held onto about others that no longer served any purpose.

3. A need to understand suffering and to learn how to transform what is occurring for themselves in simple, but straightforward ways.

4. A need to prepare spiritually for their own death. To face any fears they may have and to find a sense of peace with dying.

Addressing these needs presents an opportunity to take control of one's life. It becomes a time to embrace all the challenges presented by cancer. The times that try our souls are the ones that offer the possibility of re-discovering our true nature so that we can evolve from there. As we move from our ordinary ways of viewing things, the illusions die. The willingness to evaluate beliefs and attitudes and to release those that no longer serve us, helps increase our quality of life. It releases those patterns that have blocked our life force and allows new creative possibilities to emerge.

FINDING MEANING AND PURPOSE

So often, we are not aware of the impact and influence we have on others. My wife tells a story of a man she had never met who had a profound impact on her life. During the years of the The Great Depression, it was not unusual that her grandparents would take people on as farm workers. Having a place to stay and food in their bellies was always deeply appreciated by the people they took in. A man, educated as a geologist and unemployed, was one of these people. He carried with him a large collection of rocks that he had carefully identified. Each stone was carefully placed in an individual envelope and labeled with its name and chemical formula in an ornate European writing style.

When the man moved on, he left this large collection of stones behind. Since he was drifter at that time, there was no way to return the collection to him. Years later, my wife's grandfather gave this collection of stones to her. A young girl, she intensely studied each stone and description. Without even knowing it, he had sparked a lifelong interest and passion for science in her. He would not know that his passion would lead her to becoming a physician. We can only imagine how he felt during those tough economic times, and what he thought about his life and the direction it had taken. Chances are, he had no idea of the impact on another this part of him would eventually have.

Take some time to reflect on what events have had meaning in your life. What did others do that had a meaningful impact on your life? What kinds of things have you done that may have made a difference in the lives of others? Were there moments that seemed to be particularly significant to you?

There is a specific journey I often suggest for patients who are struggling with the meaning of their life. It is simply to go to the helping spirits and ask, "What is the meaning of my life?" or, "How can I make a difference as I prepare for the end of my life?" There are many ways to word this question. Let your senses guide you to what feels right for you.

_____

_____

_____

_____

_____

_____

_____

_____

_____

_____

_____

_____

Here are some case examples of this process:

Example #1

An oncologist refers a patient to me who at the time was deeply depressed. Diagnosed with liver cancer, she was responding to treatment. However, she is constantly exhausted. Once a professional dancer, she has lost her previous fitness. Because of this, her mind is focused on the loss of meaning in her life. She feels she has become a burden to her husband. Now in her early 40's, her entire life had been about movement. So I had her journey about how to restore purpose to her life. During her journey, she meets a dancing bear. The bear picks her up and she feels a surge of power come into her being. Although the journey lasted just a few minutes, she felt as if she and the bear had danced together for hours. While dancing, she began notice all the other animals that were watching and taking joy in the dance. The bear whispered in her ear, "Thousands have taken joy in watching you." When she returned from the journey, she gave thanks for remembering how much her life had given others. Coming out of the journey state, her mood was greatly improved. Her husband, who was participating in her counseling began to tell her the myriad of ways she had enhanced the quality of his life. Seeing the love and tears in his eyes, she was able to let go of her concerns about being a burden.

Example #2

A man in his fifties was confronting an aggressive form of prostate cancer. He and his wife were utilizing a wide mix of diet and alternative medical approaches along with surgery and chemotherapy. Though he was vibrant, he was not showing signs of improvement via the treatments and lifestyle changes. It was suggested he journey on his own behalf to meet his helping animal spirits and ask for healing assistance on his own behalf. In his journey, he met a snake that merged with his body. Watching him outwardly, his body was vibrating while he was in his journey. While merged with the snake, the snake took him to places he had lived and visited. By merging with the snake in the journey, he was able to gain information about how traditional people had learned to live in harmony with these places through the help of the spirits. He was particularly enthralled with a place in the

Peruvian Andes where the people had created an intricate irrigation system long ago. Through the movements of the snake, he sensed how the system had been modeled after the snake. He had been enthralled with the prehistoric system's ingenuity and technology. His love of these places led him to travel to some of them. Based on his journeys, he began to write a book based on what he had learned. The book wove a mix of academic and spiritually inspired information. More importantly, it was a work of love and passion for him that sustained him through the tough times. He often remarked that he felt the book was being written for him by Spirit. The book, while giving a sense of purpose to his life, also helped him in some indirect and unexpected ways heal some issues from his past. The excitement he felt led him to dream of other books. Until the very end, he believed he would write one more book. He died before holding his latest book in his hands. It came out a few days later.

HEALING RELATIONSHIPS

The diagnosis of cancer and its subsequent treatment create a broad a range of relationship issues. People with cancer now have to communicate with several new health care staff on many different levels. They have to deal with the reactions of family and friends. Then there are the co-workers who, when they learn of the diagnosis, aren't sure how to react, sometimes reacting as if cancer is contagious. Lastly, it raises issues of healing estranged relationships as they face the question of whether or not his/her life is ending.

As stated earlier in the book, the presence of loving and supportive relationships has been shown to improve possible health outcomes. In situations where there is a concern about the feelings and needs of family members, it can be helpful to journey for spiritual guidance. In the above instance, the wife is so concerned about being a burden to her husband that her depression dampens her fighting spirit. Over the years I've sat with large groups of extended family, waiting with them while a family member had surgery for cancer. While some family members asked questions that were skewed towards a positive outcome, others were filled with grief, expecting the worse. In working with cancer patients, you'll find that some want to talk about how to be or what to do. Others will worry about what will happen to them. Invariably, most patients will talk about the myriad of relationship concerns they have as they struggle with family members. Things like, "I know I'm going to die, but I'm just going to let them keep talking otherwise." Or, "I know how afraid they are that I'm leaving but I don't know how to help them." Or, "I can't take care of anymore so they'll have to figure it out themselves."

Here is a simple practice that can help you free yourself from these types of difficult ties that bind you in an unhealthy way to another individual:

Imagine yourself in a field that is familiar to you. Notice what kind of plants, flowers and trees are there. Now take time to notice your body. Where do you sense cords of attachment? These cords are beliefs and patterns that are no longer serving you or others. In your imagination find a knife or pair of scissors and cut the cords. Take time to follow each cord and see if there is someone you know on the other end. If it is someone you no longer need to be in contact with you can simply say," Thank you and goodbye." If it is someone who is a part of your life, then simply say, "I am cutting this cord as it is an old pattern that isn't helpful to either of us." Then simply acknowledge you will see them later. Take time to notice how you feel as you cut the cords away.

Now take the opportunity to do a journey to your spirit helpers for additional information and help. If there is a particular person that troubles you, ask what you can do to bring healing to it, and how you can relate to this relationship in a healthier fashion. You may have several relationships you wish to address. Or there may be other questions and concerns that arise for you. Sometimes people have found it helpful to journey for a healing ceremony for the relationship(s) in question. Remember—write down everything that happens or is said in the journey as it is all important.

JOURNEY NOTES

_____

_____

_____

_____

_____

When one faces the end of life, there are usually a number of situations where estranged relationships come to the forefront. For example, I've worked with numerous Vietnam veterans exposed to Agent Orange who later on developed non-Hodgkins lymphoma, and who, in returning home got divorced and did not maintain a relationship with their children.

One such case is Bill. Like many veterans of the Vietnam era, Bill worked for the U.S. Postal Service. He liked delivering mail because he was outdoors. He went on to explain that it was hard for him to be in closed spaces. Essentially a loner, Bill had few friends. He had a daughter in college whom he'd had only marginal contact with throughout her life. Once a year, he would visit her at Christmas. Mostly, he just sent his ex-wife support payments. Once he realized that his cancer was not responding to treatment, his journeys repeatedly directed him to make the time to say goodbye to his daughter. Although his physical condition exceeded medical expectations, his physical pain was increasing. He finally asked me if he could ask his daughter to meet with us to do some sort of a ceremony. Much to his surprise, his daughter agreed. The ceremony we created was suggested to us in a journey, and was very simply to create a sacred space where Bill and his daughter could each speak from the heart. A candle was lit, there was a prayer for healing, for compassion, and for the courage to speak the truth. In that space, Bill told his daughter that he was dying. He told her he was sorry that he had not been a larger part of her life, but that he had always been very proud of her. They both wept and he held her for a very long time. From that point on, she came to visit him daily until the day he died. At her request, he told her stories of his family and his life.

Resolving estranged relationships can be challenging, especially if the other person is deceased or unwilling to open the door to a reconciliation meeting. However, over the years I've seen many instances where journeying to spirit helpers for aid in bringing healing to a troubled relationship has been quite beneficial. These journeys can take many forms. In some cases, the journey becomes like a meeting where there is a dialogue with the estranged party. In others, the spirits may suggest a simple spiritual ceremony that brings healing and peace to the issues.

Take a moment to review the relationships in your life. Are there any that feel strained or where you feel estranged or troubled by something? If so, journey for help from the spirits on how you can bring healing to the situation.

_____

_____

_____

_____

_____

_____

_____

_____

_____

FACING FEAR AND SUFFERING

A number of patients have shared with me that when they're told they have cancer it feels like their whole life flashes before them. So this becomes a focal point for us talking about their priorities and main concerns moving forward. This is especially true when there are things that have flashed before them that they've had a particularly strong response to.

Invariably, the issue of fear and stress come up. Naturally, there are concerns about pain and suffering, for the individual and for loved ones. Facing the things we normally turn away from in fear makes us spiritually stronger, strengthening the immunology of the soul. As the soul gets stronger, its own natural ability to support healing and promote the best possible outcome increases.

We live in a culture which likes to deny the inevitability of aging and death. When we watch action films, death intrigues us. When it's real, it raises feelings of dread, queasiness, numbing or outright fear. Not everyone has fear, nor does everyone want to admit their fears. For instance, in the movie "Resurrection" we see Ellen Burstyn's character tending to her dying father who, true to his character, remains stoic. There's a brief moment where he sees the Light and brightens up. Yet he is still unable to share these emotion with her. What does the idea of death invoke in you? Are you afraid of dying? Facing these questions can strengthen our spirit, and usher in the possibility that we can ultimately be at peace with death.

Many traditional shamanic cultures look to the ancestors for help with these questions because the ancestors understand the realities of death, as well as, the celebrations and the struggles of life. Their wisdom and guidance are also sought around the challenges of life. When people think of their ancestors, many think of recently departed relatives. Quite often they reflect on the challenges and problems they had in relationship to these ancestors. As you prepare to do a journey to seek answers from your ancestors, know that you can go back many generations. In fact, you can go as far back as you need to work with ancestors, as long as it feels safe for you to do so.

In this journey, you will go to the upper world with the intention of meeting an ancestor who can help you alleviate any fear and suffering you have in regards to your illness. Be aware that you may need to go to a different level of the upper world, traveling through more than one layer to get where you need to go.

JOURNEY NOTES

_____

_____

_____

_____

_____

_____

_____

_____

_____

Here is a case example of this journey:

An African American male in his mid-forties had lung cancer. He was facing the removal of a lung and further treatment. He admitted that not being able to breathe scared the hell out of him. He had no family and, as a child, was bounced from foster home to foster home. During his life he had worked at variety of labor jobs and he had been married twice. He admitted that he had a hard time being close to anyone, and said that his marriage ended because he refused to talk about things with his wife. From his view of the world in the 1980's, he saw the whole world as superficial. He felt this superficiality made it easier for him to hide out emotionally. Initially, he was extremely resistant to journeying to his ancestors because all he knew about his family was its history of violence. He eventually agreed to journey way back in time.

In the journey, he met an African ancestor during the time of the slave trade. This ancestor told him that family had turned against family and that it was a hard time. "They need to be forgiven," he says. When asked about how to face his fear about breathing, the ancestor took him to a river. Together, they went underwater. The fact that he could breathe while submerged in water startled him. The ancestor told him to remember, and as he did he felt the water flowing through him as if he were being cleansed.

After the journey, the man said he could breathe a little more freely. I suggested that we go to the nearby lake and spend some time together by the water. Once we were there, he decided to strip to down to his undershorts and jump in. When he came up out of the water, he said he had felt a sense of calm while there. As a result of this experience, he decided to spend as much time as he could visiting the lake. He had found a way to make the journey real to him in his everyday life.

Death is not always an end. It may also be a new beginning. In the natural world, what looks like death may be rebirth and change. Years ago, I witnessed the fires in Yellowstone National Park. The land and many trees were blackened by the fires. In those areas, nothing looked alive. When I returned years later, the areas that had appeared dead were covered in beautiful flowers. Before the fires there were so many trees the flowers could not grow. Nature's message to us, I believe, is this: By embracing death in its spiritual form, we see the possibility that death may not be what we imagine it to be.

In the next journey, go to one of your spirit helpers and ask to meet the spirit of death. Your intent is to learn more about its purpose, but also to ask Death to help you with your healing. Like any of the journeys in this book, it is up to you to determine if this feels right for you to do.

JOURNEY NOTES

_____

_____

_____

_____

_____

_____

_____

_____

_____

_____

_____

_____

_____

_____

_____

_____

_____

_____

_____

_____

_____

_____

_____

_____

_____

_____

_____

_____

_____

_____

_____

Here are a couple of examples of this journey:

Example #1

Ellen was a nursing home patient diagnosed with inoperable brain cancer. A religious Christian woman, she was open to doing the spiritual imagery work as long as it didn't go against her religion. She did an upperworld journey and Jesus told her it was ok, so she went with him to meet the spirit of death. To her, death looked like the grim reaper. She asked him if it was her time to go. The grim reaper shook his head, "no". She then asked him if he could help her. He grabbed her by the hand and took her to her family home where her 90-year-old sister still lived. He told her she must go there and live, too. Then he waved his hand over her head. Two weeks later she returned home to live with her sister. Inexplicably, her tumor shrunk by 50 percent and she felt well enough to return to her own home Her doctor agreed. She then looked at her doctor and said, "Death doesn't want me quite yet."

Example #2

An 8-year-old boy with a diagnosis of leukemia asked if he was going to die. His parents, who came to our group seeking healing assistance to augment his medical treatment, responded to his question with, "It's in God's hands." The young boy wanted to learn how to talk with God so we had him do a simple upper world journey to meet a spirit helper. He met the spirit of death who told him he was his helper. The boy asked him why he was causing so much suffering for his family. Death replied, "It is not so, there is so much love." Death then showed him all the love his family felt while supporting him in his treatments. His saw that his siblings gave up time with friends because they wanted to be with him. Death told him that it was important to return the love. After the journey, he boy reported feeling light headed but good all over. His demeanor was much brighter as he asked to do more journeys to his teacher.

Preparing Spiritually for Death Though every journey the shaman takes is considered a mini death and an exploration of where the soul goes upon death, there are a number of journeys that help a person prepare for death.

Shamans explore the realms of death to learn about where souls go. Traditionally, it has been a role of tribal shamans to help the souls of the departed transition from the earthly plain. Many of the journeys that help prepare one for death are best done with the assistance of a skilled counselor knowledgeable about these methods.

It's been my experience that there is no one way to help someone to prepare. Some people find comfort in telling stories about their lives and being able to say goodbye to their loved ones. A number of people have had their stories recorded by oral historians as a way of passing on their stories to future generations.

Others who have completed many of the suggestions highlighted in this book, are in a place of acceptance, clear that their time has come. Some will journey for ceremonies that will help them say goodbye to friends and family. Through the years, a number of people have chosen to have a funeral before they died, so they could hear the eulogies. They also wanted to express appreciations to the significant people in their lives. Simply said, each of us is unique and each of us is the same. Our needs at the end of life are diverse. One size does not fit all.

There are a couple of different journeys offered here as opportunity to begin the process. Patients often wonder who will be there for them when they die. That wondering lays the groundwork for this journey. Simply ask, "Who will be there when I die?" The best journey for this is an upper world journey, and it is one you can do whether you are currently ill or not.

_____

_____

_____

_____

_____

_____

_____

_____

_____

_____

_____

_____

_____

_____

_____

_____

_____

_____

_____

_____

_____

_____

_____

_____

_____

_____

_____

_____

_____

_____

_____

_____

_____

_____

_____

Here is a case example of this journey:

Helen was living with her family. She had cancer throughout her entire body. Despite her many care needs, Helen had a strong fighting spirit and a desire to die with dignity. She often challenged her nursing care, championing the cause of all those receiving nursing care. She confronted any perceived inconsistencies. Somehow, she went well beyond what seemed medically possible given the spread of her cancer. Everyone described her as a "ball of fire."

She journeyed to learn who would be there for her when she died. Her husband and some of their children were there to greet her. She had experienced many losses in her life and was overwhelmed emotionally by meeting them in her journey. Her oldest daughter held her and told her they were waiting for her. Her daughter went on to say that she was very loved. Returning from the journey, she admitted that she had thought it would feel like pretending but said that it had felt very real to her. Teary eyed, she told stories of how her children had died and the ache that she had carried in her heart all her life. She felt that somehow her children were telling her that it was all OK, which was a great comfort to her.

When some people are facing death, they will ask for something akin to homework. They want to know what they can do to prepare. Perhaps they've read books about various spiritual traditions. Regardless, they have concerns they want to address before they die. A journey I sometimes suggest for this involves going to the place where there is a life review. Some people who have had near-death experiences often talk about experiencing a life review. In the dreaming tradition of my great aunt, there is a place between here and the place where souls go upon death. It is a place to dream to for life review and cleaning one's slate. To clean one's slate simply means that soul unburdens itself, releasing past mistakes and opening up the opportunity to live life differently.

In this journey, hold the intent of going to a place on the cusp of the middle world and the upper world. This place is a place where compassionate, non-judgmental beings review your life with you. Once there, express your intent of learning through a review of your life. There may be questions there for you such as "Did you love well?" "What did you learn?" "What did you give or share of yourself?" Simply note what you are shown, and take it as an opportunity to learn and to work to bring healing changes.

JOURNEY NOTES

_____

_____

_____

_____

_____

_____

_____

_____

_____

_____

_____

_____

_____

_____

DEATH, DREAMING, AND REMEMBERING

Here's a case example of this journey:

A 60-year-old woman with breast cancer journeyed to the place of life review. She was met by several people in simple white robes. They asked her questions about how she thought she did in life. Her answers were simple but honest. She felt she loved well, but could have done better. She could have shown more caring at times. She wished she had spent more time with her children when they were little. A giant book is opened and they say to her, "Yes, this is true." The book then shifted into something like a Rolodex and as the pages flipped, images from different times in her life appeared to her. She took note of the different scenes presented to her. In her heart, sensing they were important. After the journey was over, she felt compelled to spend some time sharing her regrets with each of her children. She later reported back that her efforts were well received and actually brought her and her daughters closer.

FINAL THOUGHTS

In my last dreaming with my great aunt, she told me to bury all the stories I had written. Through the years, she had encouraged me to write down what I had learned from others, from her, from personal observation. She said it was time to give them away. She encouraged the idea of burying them as a treasure so years later someone would find them. "Stories are like bread for the soul. You keep working them and something will rise," she said.

I hope this book provides comfort and insights for your healing. As you work your healing path, reshaping the stories of your life and evolving your relationship with yourself, to others, and to your illness, take time to appreciate the learning you have taken from your efforts.

Peace
with
Cancer

Bibliography

ARTICLES

Achterberg, Jeanne, K. Cooke, R. Richards, L. Standish, L. Kozak, and J. Lake. "Evidence of for Correlations Between Distant Intentionality and Brain Function in Recipients: A Functional Magnetic Resonance Imaging Analysis." *Journal of Alternative and Complementary Medicine* 11, no.6 (2005),965-071

Balkwill, F. and A. Mantovani. "Inflammation and Cancer; Back to Virchow?" *Lancet,* 357, no.9255(2001), pp.539-45

Bond, Hillary. "Punishing Terrains: The Land Strikes Back." *Shamanism: Journal of Foundation for Shamanic Studies,* vol.19(2), pp.26-35, 2006

Cunningham, Alastair. "How Psychological Therapy May Prolong Survival in Cancer Patients: New Evidence and a Simple Theory." *Integrative Cancer Therapies,* vol.3, no.3, 214-229, 2004

Davis, Devra Lee and Pamela Webster. "The Social Context of Science: Cancer and the Environment." *Annals of the American Academy of Political and Social Science,* 2002, 584; 13-34

Dvorak, H.F., "Tumors: Wounds That Do Not Heal: Similarities Between Tumor Stroma Generation and Wound Healing." *New England Journal of Medicine,* 315, no.26, (1986):3650-59

Engle, Gillian. "Promoting Peace in Integrating Western and Indigenous Healing Traditions." *Peace and Conflict: Journal of Peace Psychology,* 1998:4 (3)

Eshowsky, Myron. "Shamanic Work with Cancer and Other Aggressive Illnesses." *Shamanism,* vol.20 (1), pp.3-8, Spring/Summer 2007

Eshowsky, Myron. "Shamanism and the Healing of History." *Voices: The Art and Science and Psychotherapy Journal,* Spring 2006, Vol.42(1):79-85.

Eshowsky, Myron. "Shamanism and Peacemaking." *Shamanism,* vol.12 (2), pp.4-9, Fall/Winter 1999

Eshowsky, Myron. "The Spirit of Place and the Healing of History." *Shamanism,* vol.14 (2):pp.6-12, Fall/Winter 2001

Goldschmidt, Walter. "Peacemaking and the Institutions of Peace in Tribal Societies." *The Anthropology of Peace and Non-Violence,* Leslie Sponsel and Thomas Gregor, eds., Boulder, Lynne Rienner Publishers, 1994

Guirgus-Blake, Janelle. "Cancer Genertic Risk Assessment for Individuals at Risk of Familial Breast Cancer." *American Family Physician,* vol.77, no.4, Feb. 2008, pp.449-450

Hayes, Jasmeet Pannu; Kevin LaBar; Christopher Petry; Gregory McCarthy; Rajendra Morey. "Alterations in the Neural Circuitry for Emotion and Attention Associated with Post Traumatic Stress Symptomatology." *Psychiatric Research Neuroimmaging,* 172, 3009, 7-15

Horrigan, Bonnie. "Shamanic Healing: We Are Not Alone." an interview with Michael Harner, Ph.D., *Alternative Therapies,* 1996, 2(3)

Lund, Jacques. "Words in the Night: The Ceremonial Dialogue—One Expression of Peaceful Relationships among the Yanomami." in *The Anthropology of Peace and Non-Violence,* Leslie Sponsel and Thomas Gregor, eds., Boulder, Lynee Rienner Publishers, 1994

Moleman, Nico, M.D., Jan B.F. Hulscher, M.Sc., Onno van der Hart, Ph.D., and Gert. Scheepstra, M.D., "The Effect of Multiple Personality Disorder on Anesthesia: A Case Report." *Dissociation,* vol.VII, no.1, September 1991, pp.197-199

Neher, A. "Auditory Driving Observed with Scalp Electrodes in Normal Subjects." *Electroneuroencephalography and Clinical Neurophysiology Journal,* 1962:13, 449-451

Miller, S.D. and Triggiano, P.J., "The Psychophysiologic Investigation of Multiple Personality Disorder." *American Journal of Clinical Hypnosis,* 1992, 35, pp.47-61

Maxfield, Melinda. "The Journey of the Drum." *ReVision,* 1994: 16,148-156

Ventegodt, Soren, et al. "Clinical Holistic Medicine: Metastatic Cancer." *The Scientific World Journal,* (2004), 4,913-935

Ventegodt, Soren, et al. "Clinical Holistic Medicine: Induction of Spontaneous Remission of Cancer by Recovery of the Human Character and the Purpose of Lif.," *The Scientific World Journal,* (2004) 4, 362-377

Van der Kolk, Bessel. "Disorders of Extreme Stress: The Empirical Formulations of Complex Adaptation to Trauma." *Journal of Traumatic Stress,* (2005) 389

Walsh, Roger. "What is a Shaman? Definition, Origin and Distribution." *Journal of TransPersonal Psychology,* 1989, vol.21:1-11

White, M. and M. Verhoef. "Cancer as Part of the Journey: The Role of Spirituality in the Decision to Decline Conventional Prostate Treatment and Use Complimentary and Alternative Medicine." *Integrative Cancer Therapies,* 5(2), 117-122, 2006

BOOKS

Abram, David, *The Spell of the Sensuous*. New York: Vintage Books, 1996

Achterberg, Jeanne, *Imagery and Healing: Shamanism and Modern Medicine*. Boston: Shambhala Books, 1985

Achterberg, Jeanne O., Carl Simonton, and Stephanie Matthews-Simonton. *Stress, Psychological Factors, and Cancer*. Fort Worth, Texas: New Medicine Press, 1976

Block, Keith I., M.D. *Life Over Cancer: The Block Center Program for Integrative Cancer Treatment*. New York: Bantam Books, 2009

Bunker, Stephen G., *The Snake With Golden Braids*. Lanham: Lexington Books, 2006

Davis, Devra. *Secret History of the War on Cancer*. New York: Basic Books, 2007

Doore, Gary. ed. *Shaman's Path: Healing, Personal Growth and Empowerment*. Boston: Shambhala Books, 1988

Egendorf, Arthur. *Healing from the War: Trauma and Transformation after Viet Nam*. Boston: Houghton Mifflin, 1985

Eliade, Mircea. *Shamanism: Archaic Techniques of Ecstasy*. Princeton: Princeton University Press, 1964

Faguet, Guy B. *The War on Cancer: An Anatomy of Failure, A Blueprint for the Future*. Dordrecht, The Netherlands: Springer, 2008

Fuan, Yi-Fi. *Landscapes of Fear*. New York: Pantheon Books, 1998

Greenspan, Miriam. *Healing through the dark emotions: The wisdom of grief, fear, and despair*. Boston: Shambhala, 2004

Geffen, Jeremy, M.D. *The Journey Through Cancer: Healing and Transforming the Whole Person*. New York: Three Rivers Press, 2006

Grossman, Lt. Col. Dave. *On Killing: The Psychological Cost of Learning to Kill in War and Society*. New York: Back Bay Books, 1996

Halifax, Joan. *Shamanic Voices: A Survey of Visionary Narratives*. New York: E. P. Dutton, 1979

Harner, Michael. *The Way of the Shaman*. San Francisco: Harper, 1990

Hirshberg, Caryle and Marc Ian Barasch. *Remarkable Recovery: What Extraordinary Healings Tell Us About Getting Well and Staying Well*. New York: Riverhead Books, 1995

Ingerman, Sandra. *Medicine for the Earth: How to Transform Personal and Environmental Toxins*. New York: Three Rivers Press, 2000

Ingerman, Sandra. *Soul Retrieval: Mending the Fragmented Self*. San Francisco: HarperCollins, 1991

Katz, Richard, Megan Biesele and Verna St.Dennis. *Healing Makes Our Hearts Happy: Spirituality and Cultural Transformation among the Kalahari Ju!* Rochester, Vermont: Inner Traditions. 1997

Kramer, Chaim. *Rebbe Nachman of Bratslav: Anatomy of the Soul*. New York: Bratslav Research Institute, 1998

Lerner, Michael. *Choices in Healing: Integrating the Best of Conventional and Complementary Approaches to Cancer*. Cambridge MA: MIT Press, 1994

Lewis, C. S. *A Grief Observed*. New York: Bantam Books, 1976

Lipton, Bruce. *The Biology of Belief: Unleashing the Power of Consciousness, Matter, & Miracles*. Santa Rosa, CA: Mountain of Love/ Elite Books, 2005

Mander, Jerry and Victoria Tauli-Corpuz. *Paradigm Wars: Indigenous Peoples' Resistance to Globalization*. San Francisco, CA: Sierra Club Books, 2006

Mangano, Joseph J. *Low Level Radiation and Immune System Damage*. New York: Lewis Publishers, 1999

Micozzi, M.S., ed. *Fundamentals of Complementary and Alternative Medicine*. Philadelphia: Churchill Livingston, 2001

Mindell, Arnold. *Leader as Martial Artist*. Portland: Lao Tse Press, 2000

Okri, Ben. *The Famished Road*. New York: Anchor Books, 1991

O'Regan, Brendan and Carlyle Hirshberg. *Spontaneous Remission: An Annotated Bibliography*. Sausalito: Institute of Noetic Sciences, 1993

Palmer, Wendy. *The Practice of Freedom: Aikido Practices as a Spiritual Guide*. Berkeley: Rodmell Press, 2001

Palmer, Parker. *The Courage to Teach*. San Francisco: Josey Bass, 1998

Putnam, Frank. *Diagnosis and Treatment of Multiple Personality Disorder*. New York: Guilford Press, 1989

Ross, Colin. *The Osiris Complex*. Toronto: University of Toronto Press, 1994

Rossi, Ernest. *The Psychobiology of Gene Expression*. New York: W.W.Norton and Company, 2002

Sanders, Barry. *The Green Zone: The Environmental Coasts of Militarism*. Oakland: AK Press, 2009

Schmookler, Andrew Bard. *Living Posthumously: Confronting the Loss of Vital Powers*. New York: Henry Holt and Company, 1997

Scaer, Robert C. *The Body Bears the Burden: Trauma, Dissociation, and Disease*. New York: Haworth Medical Press, 2001

Servan-Schreiber, David. *Anticancer: A New Way of Life*. New York: Viking, 2007

Silver, Julie K., M.D. *What Helped Me Get Through: Cancer Survivors Share Wisdom and Hope*. Atlanta: American Cancer Society, 2009

Steingraber, Sandra. *Living Downstream: An Ecologist Looks at Cancer and the Environment*. Reading, MA: Addison-Wesley Publishing Company, 1997

Sternberg, Edith M., M.D. *The Balance Within: The Science Connecting Health and Emotions*. New York: W H Freeman and Company, 2001

Stirling, M.W., *Historical and Ethnographic Material on the Jivaro Indians*. Bureau of American Ethnology Bulletin 117. Washington, D.C.: Smithsonian Institution, 1938

Strasser, Judith. *Facing Fear: Cancer and Politics, Courage and Hope*. Madison,WI: Borderland Books, 2008

Temoshok, Lydia, Ph.D. and Henry Dreher. *The Type C Connection: The Behavioral Links to Cancer and Your Health*. New York, Random House, 1997

Terkel, Studs. *Will The Circle Be Unbroken? Reflections on Death, Rebirth, and Hunger for a Faith*. New York: Ballantine Books, 2001

Tick, Ed. *War and the Soul: Healing Our Nation's Veterans from Post-Traumatic Stress Disorder*. Wheaton, IL: Quest Books, 2005

Van der Kolk,Bessel A., Alexander McFarlane, and Lars Weisaeth, editors. *Traumatic Stress: The Effects of Overwhelming Experience on Mind,Body, and Society*. New York: The Guilford Press, 1996

Weingarten, Kaethe. *Common Shock: Witnessing Violence Every Day*. New York: Dutton, 2003

Winkelman, Michael. *Shamanism:The Neural Ecology of Consciousness and Healing*. Westport, CT: Bergin and Garvey, 2000

Yalom, Irvin D. *Staring at the Sun: Overcoming the Terror of Death*. San Francisco: Jossey Bass, 2008

Chapter Footnotes

INTRODUCTION

[1] Eliade, Mircea. Shamanism, *Archaic Techniques of Ectasy*, Princeton, Princeton University Press, 1974, p.5

[2] Winkelman, Michael. *Shamanism: The Neural Ecology of Consciousness and Healing*, Westport, CN, Bergin and Garvey, 2000, p.xi

[3] Harner, Michael. *The Way of the Shaman*, San Francisco, Harper and Row, 1990, p.xxii

CHAPTER 1

[1] Altschuler, Lise and Karolyn. A. Gazella. *Definitive Guide to Cancer*, Berkeley, Celestial Arts, 2007, p.22

[2] Sorensen,T.I.A., G.G.Nielsen, P.K.Andersent,et al. "Genetics and Environmental Influences on Premature Death in Adult Adoptees." *New England Journal of Medicine*, 318 (1988):727-32

Also noted:

Lichtenstein,P., N.V. Holm, P.K. Verkasalo, et al. "Environmental and Heritable Factors in the Causation of Cancer—Analyses of Cohorts of Twins from Sweden, Denmark, and Finland." *New England Journal of Medicine*, 343, no.2(2000): 78=85

[3] Stengraber, Sandra. *Living Downstream: An Ecologist Looks at Cancer and the Environment.* Reading, MA, Addison-Wesley Publishing Co, 1997;

Davis, Devra. *Secret History of the War on Cancer*, New York, Basic Books, 2007

Davis, Devra and Pamela Webster, "The Social Context of Science: Cancer and the Environment." Annals of the American Academy of Political and Social Sciences, 2002 ,584,13-34

[4] Faguet, Guy B. *The War on Cancer: An Anatomy of Failure, A Blueprint for the Future.* Dordrecht, The Netherlands, Springer, 2008, p.53

[5] Servan-Schreiber, David. *Anticancer: A New Way of Life.* New York,Viking, 2007 p.26

[6] Davis, Devra. *Secret History of the War on Cancer*, New York, Basic Books, 2007 pp.39-40

[7] Lerner, Michael. *Choices in Healing: Integrating the Best of Conventional and Complimentary Approaches to Cancer.* Cambridge, MA, MIT Press, 1994, pp.13-14

[8] White, M. and M.Verhoef. "Cancer as Part of the Journey: The Role of Spirituality in the Decision to Decline Conventional Prostate Treatment and the Use of Complimentary and Alternative Medicine." *Integrative Cancer Therapies*, 5(2),117-122, 2006

CHAPTER 2

1 Achterberg, J.; Simonton and Simonton, 1976, p.3

2 John Hopkins Study, *New England Journal of Medicine*, Feb.8,2001

3 Lerner, Mark. American Academy of Experts in Traumatic Stress website

4 Temoshook, Lydia, Ph.D. and Henry Dreher. *The Type C Connection:The Behavioral Links to Cancer and Your Heatlh*, New York, Random House, 1997

5 Achterberg, J. Simonton and Mathews-Simonton,1976

6 Halifax, Joan. *Shamanic Voices*, p.5

7 Achterberg, J. "The Wounded Healer" in *Gary Doore, Shaman's Path*, p116

8 Achterberg, J. Simonton and Simonton, 1976

CHAPTER 3

1 Lewis, C. S. *A Grief Observed*, N.Y., Bantam Books, 1976, pp13-14

2 Mindell, Arnold. *Leader as Martial Artist*, Portland, Lao Tse Press, 2000, p.16

3 Block, Keith. *Life Over Cancer: The Block Center Program for Integrative Cancer Treatment*, N.Y., Bantam Books, 2009, p.215

CHAPTER 4

1 White, Theodore. *The Once and Future King*, p.183

2 Moleman, Nico M.D., Jan B.F. Hulscher, M.Sc., Onno van der Hart, Ph.D., and Gert. L. Scheepstra, M.D. "The Effect of Multiple Personality Disorder on Anesthesia: A Case Report", *Dissociation*, vol. VII, No. 1, September, 1991

also, Miller, S. D. and Triggiano, P.J. "The Psychophysiologic investigation of multiple personality disorder: Review and update. *American Journal of Clinical Hypnosis,*(1992)35, 476-61

3 Mulhern, Sherril. *Psychiatric Centers of the Americas Journal*, 1973

CHAPTER 5

1 Quote of Dr. Ahmad Harden, World Health Organization, in Britta Mae Rose's "America's Radioactive War", *CounterPunch*, November 11, 2004